CW00538361

SCANNER BUSTERS 2

How to Beat the Electronic Ban on Scanning

by D C Poole

INTERPRODUCTS

Publishers of Specialist Radio Books

Scotland and Eire

Scanner Busters 2

© Copyright by Interproducts, 1996

All rights reserved. No part of this book may be reproduced or transmitted in any form or by any means electronic or mechanical, including photocopying, recording or by any information storage and retrieval systems, without permission in writing from the publisher except in the case of brief quotations embodied in critical articles and reviews.

ISBN 0 9519783 1 4. 1st edition September 1994
ISBN 1 900445 02 6 2nd edition May 1996

This book is sold *as is*, without warranty of any kind, either express or implied, respecting the contents of this book, including but not limited to implied warranties for the book's quality, performance, merchantibility, ir fitness for any particular purpose. Neither Interproducts nor its dealers or distributors shall be liable to the purchaser or any other person or entity with respect to any liablity, loss or damage caused, alleged to be caused directly or indirectly by this book. This book is designed and compiled purely for entertainment and educational purposes, and is not intended to be used in conjunction with any type or form of VHF/UHF scanning receiver, which may be in direct contravention of the Wireless Telegraphy Act, or as a professional guide. Neither the author nor the publisher accept any responsibility for errors or omissions present in the text.

Front cover photograph a Philips PRP74 portable radio by courtesy of Philips Telecom.

UK Office:
   8 Abbot Street, Perth, PH2 0EB, Scotland.
   Telephone and Fax:: 01738-441199.

Contents

Introduction

While it is only two years since the first edition of this book was launched it seems more like ten. Since then the rate of technological change in the radio communications industry has been incredible. Some of the systems I described such as GSM digital cellular telephones were then in their infancy but now digital phones outsell analogue ones. Likewise two years ago MASC scrambled radios were only used by special squads in a few police forces, now they are coming much more common. In this new edition of *Scanner Busters* I will explain how these systems and other new ones work, what they sound like and if it is possible to monitor them on your scanner. Don't worry this isn't a textbook full of theory and you don't need a degree in electronics or mathematics, but if you don't want to be caught by surprise by radical changes in what you will soon be hearing then this is the book to read.

It wouldn't have been possible to write this book without the help of Richard Drabble, Sonya Saxby, John Driver, Philips Communications Systems, Icom (UK) Ltd., Racal Cougar Ltd., Mercury One to One Ltd and Alcatel.

D C Poole
May 1996

Digital Trunking Systems 1

In the previous edition I described analogue trunking systems such as MPT 1327. While these systems use digital methods to transmit the computer instructions on their control channel, all voice channel transmissions use narrow band frequency modulation (FM) which as I mentioned can be received on any scanner. Digital trunking systems however turn all speech into binary 1's and 0's (just like GSM phones) which are then transmitted using special modulation methods. This gives a digital trunked network several advantages over its analogue counterpart.

1) Spectral efficiency. In simple terms this means more users can be fitted onto less frequencies.
2) It is more secure as it cannot be received on a standard scanner also it is much easier to encrypt.
3) The binary 1's and 0's can be used to send any kind of information over the system such as computer data, voices or even pictures.

With all these advantages it was inevitable that digital trunked systems would be developed, but if each manufacturer came up with its own system there would be many problems. Mobile radios from one company would not be compatible with base stations with another, costs would be higher and each manufacturer's system would probably operate on different frequencies. For this reason European governments in the 1980's asked the various companies to get together and come up with a common standard for trunked radio networks. They did this and the standard they devised is known as TETRA (Trans European Trunked Radio). Although TETRA can be used by the likes of taxi firms and delivery companies it was always intended that it would be used by all the European emergency services. This offers many advantages for international police co-operation. If Dutch police are watching a drug smuggler they could use their normal handheld radio to talk to their colleagues in the German police to warn them about the smuggler. Likewise the police in Northern Ireland will be able to easily contact the police in Eire while patroling the border. At the moment the police in these countries not only use different radio systems but different frequencies. As TETRA will be used by all of a countries emergency services it will make communications between them both quicker and easier. An ambulance rushing an accident victim to hospital will be able to talk directly to traffic police to tell them which road junctions to close so they can get to the hospital faster. At the moment an ambulance has to radio this information to its own control centre which then has to telephone the police control room who finally radios the information to the police radio officers which leads to delays.

As you will probably expect the TETRA standard is very long and very complicated but the basics of it can be simplified. The modulation system used is known as DQPSK (Differential Quadrature Phase Shift Keying) this is very clever because it allows two binary bits to be sent at one time (unlike the modulation system used in GSM phones which can only send one bit at a time). The actual data is transmitted at 18000 bits a second but because two bits are sent at once the actual rate is really 36000 bits a second. This is much faster than the data sent on a MPT1327's system control channel which is only 1200 bits a second. TETRA allows up to four users to use one frequency at the same time. It does this by splitting the frequency into four fragments of time each 20 milli seconds long called slots. Each user is given a time slot in which they receive or transmit information (again like GSM phones).

A TETRA data burst

Each TETRA data burst is 0.06 seconds long

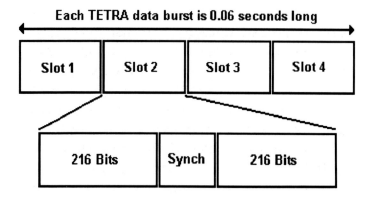

The slots do not always carry digitised voice they are also used to send instructions to the mobile radios on the network such as to tell a radio it is being called.

The system will allow one user to use all four slots if needed. One such case where this could be handy would be where a police car is chasing a stolen car. The TETRA radio in the police car could use one slot for the policeman in the car to talk to other police officers while the other three slots could be used to transmit pictures of the chase from a small camera in the police car back to the control room.

A TETRA radio system has three control channels and however many traffic channels (which carry the time slots with digitised voice) as are required. The three control channels are:-

1) The fast control channel. This channel is the one which mobiles register with when they join the network. It is also the one which instructs a radio when during a conversation it should change to a different traffic channel.
2) The broadcast channel. This one is used to transmit information about the base station and the frequencies it uses. It also transmits information about neighbouring base stations. This channel can be recognised by a listener as it contains bursts of 2.25 kHz audio tone. These bursts enable the computers in the mobile radios to ensure their internal clock is synchronised to that of the computer in the base station.
3) The slow control channel. This is the channel used by the base station to signal to mobile radios that other radios are calling them.

I think the best way to describe how a TETRA radio will work is to give an example of its use. Imagine a traffic policeman starting his shift after briefing he walks over to his patrol car and turns on his TETRA radio. The radio then scans the entire frequency band it has been allocated looking for broadcast channels. When it has found the one with the strongest signal it downloads information one that base station and also on neighbouring base stations. Then the radio tunes to the fast control channel (it found the frequency from information downloaded from the broadcast channel) where it transmits the radio's identity number and asks to register with the base station. This then checks the radios identity number against a list of the identity numbers of stolen radios. As the radio isn't on this list the base station transmits on the fast control channel confirming that the mobile radio is now registered on the network and can make and receive calls. The mobile radio now monitors the slow control channel. After ten minutes the police control room receives a call reporting an accident on the motorway. The police dispatcher decides to give the job to our police officer by radio. He types the officers callsign into his computer and starts to talk. At this point the base station transmits on the slow control channel instructing the officers radio to go to traffic channel three and listen to slot one where there is a call from the dispatcher. The officer's radio displays the word "DISPATCHER" on a small screen on its front panel. The radio also tunes to traffic channel three where it takes the binary data from slot one and turns it into audio which is then broadcast from the patrol cars speaker. While receiving the message about the motorway accident the officer drives over the brow of a hill and the signal from the base station starts to fade. At this point the mobile radio checks the signal strength of all neighbouring base station broadcast channels (it found out the frequencies of these from the information it downloaded from the broadcast channel when it first logged on) and finds the strongest one. It then signals on that base stations fast control channel that it would like to register. The new base station then talks to the old base station and finds out that a call is in progress so it signals on its fast control channel that the mobile is registered and that it should tune to traffic channel two slot four. This all happens in a fraction of a second and the police officer doesn't even notice a break in the voice of his dispatcher !

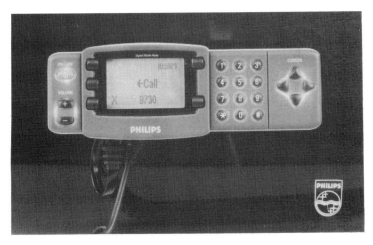

A Philips TETRA digital mobile radio
Photo courtesy of Philips Telecom

Just as the GSM system has its own encryption system A5 defined as part of the standard, TETRA also has its own encryption system however no details have leaked about this system (not even a name!) and it is not clear if all TETRA radios will use it.

Although no TETRA systems have been commissioned yet TETRA is not just a pipe dream. The European Community has ordered that all publicly funded digital radio systems must use TETRA. The worlds first TETRA system is to be used by the police on the Island of Jersey where a system made by Motorola will be operational by the end of 1996. It is planned that all the British emergency services will be using TETRA in the next decade. A frequency band 380 MHz to 400 MHz which is currently used by military aircraft will be cleared and will be used by all European emergency services using TETRA. The other frequencies to be used by TETRA are 410 MHz to 430 MHz, 450 to 470 MHz and 870 to 888 MHz.

TETRA isn't the only digital trunking system in existence however there are several others. The main competitor in Europe is made by the French company Matra and is known as MATRACOM 9600 but also TETRAPOL. It uses GMSK (Gaussian Minimum Shift Keying) modulation just like GSM phones but at a lower data rate of 8000 bits a second. It can do all the things TETRA can do and uses an unknown encryption system. Unlike TETRA however this system is in widespread operational use as I write this. The French

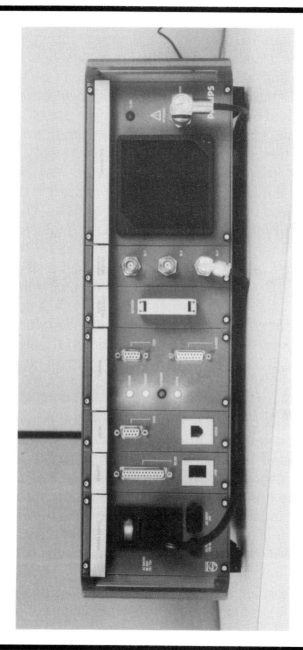

A Philips TETRA base station
Photo courtesy of Philips Telecom

Gendarmerie have a national network using it called RUBIS. It is also used by the French national railway police and also by the Catalan police in Spain. Another Digital trunking system is AEGIS which is made by Ericsson of Sweden. Existing users of this company's EDACS analogue trunking system can upgrade their system to AEGIS. Motorola sell a digital system known as ASTRO. This system has sold very well in the United States where it is used in the 800 MHz band by law enforcement agencies such as the Florida Highway Patrol and the Los Angeles police Department. ASTRO doesn't have to be used in trunked systems it can also be used on a single frequency. In Britain the South Wales police firearms squad use ASTRO radios like this. The Americans are also trying to define a single standard for emergency services digital communications. This is known as APCO 25 or Project 25. At the moment no project 25 radios have been manufactured but it will happen.

One other Europe wide digital trunking system being planned is the Pan-European Railway system. This is needed because as European railways become more integrated, due to projects like the Channel Tunnel, there is a need for a common radio system. At the moment each national railway uses it own radio network. If the plan works all European trains will be fitted with one of these radios, this means a French SNCF train from Lyon on its way to London can be warned about an accident on the line by signal staff in Kent. It seems the committee planning the system are going to adopt a form of the GSM phone standard but with the addition of the group call feature. Group call is the ability say of the signal staff in Kent to be able to press a button and talk to all the trains under his control simultaneously. This is not supported in the current GSM standard where each train would have to be called separately. There has been pressure for the committee just to use the TETRA standard. Whatever standard they choose a Europe wide frequency allocation has been allocated for the system. This is 915 MHz to 919 MHz (base transmit) and 870 MHz to 874 MHz (mobile transmit).

I am certain that within ten years all emergency services will be using digital TETRA radios. Many companies who run commercial analogue trunked networks also plan to use TETRA. Whether or not scanner hobbyists are going to be able to monitor TETRA depends on one thing - encryption! If encryption isn't used all scanner manufacturer has to do to build a TETRA capable scanner would be to buy the standards documents from ETSI (the European Technical Standards Institute) and employ some talented engineers, but such a scanner would be no good if encryption is used. However while encryption does add voice security it gives organisations and companies who use it a whole load of hassle. They have to ensure that all their radios are loaded with the current encryption key. If the radios have to communicate with those of another organisation they must also have their encryption key. If a radio is stolen then it is possible the thief may be able to extract the key so all the remaining radios must have a new key loaded. While the police probably need this level of voice security the ambulance and fire services possibly don't won't want encryption and all the work it requires. So I don't expect TETRA will wipe out scanning although you will have to buy an expensive new TETRA ready scanner when they come on sale.

Pagers 2

R adio pagers have been around since the 1960's but it wasn't until the late 1980's when integrated circuits (chips) were developed for pagers which reduced them in size and price. As I write this it is possible to buy a small and light pager with a built in display for under £50. Until recently most pagers were owned by people whose job required that they need be called away from home at short notice such as doctors. But due to the rapid fall in price and some very aggressive marketing by paging companies all sorts of interesting people use them now. The Police are now major users of them. In North Yorkshire for example the force uses them as a way to defeat criminals equipped with scanners. If a burglar is reported as being seen breaking into a building then instead of using UHF radio to inform their officers and possibly alerting the burglar if he had a scanner. Instead the officers are told to attend the incident by a message on their pager. It also seems that most plain clothes CID officers now carry pagers. The private security sector is also a major user of pagers. In many city centres the store detectives of the various large shops have formed warning networks using pagers. When one store detective spots a well known shop lifter she can ring a telephone number and give a description of the thief which is then broadcast as a text message to all the store detectives on the paging system

Then all of them are on the alert. Another such scheme is often called "Pub Watch" when the managers of public houses in a city centre set up a similar network to warn each other of trouble makers. If a hooligan causes trouble in one pub the manager of that pub can quickly circulate his description making it highly unlikely he will be able to get into any other pubs. There are several different kinds of notification networks using pagers including one for birdwatchers which informs them when a rare bird is spotted. Surfers use Mercury pagers to let one another know where surfing conditions are good !

There are several pager message standards but by far the most common in Europe and around the world is known as POCSAG (Post Office Code Standardisation Advisory Group). This was originally devised by the British post office in the early 1970's. In Britain there are three national paging systems. These are:-
British Telecom between 153.025 MHz and 153.500 MHz.
Mercury on 138.175 MHz.
Hutchinson Telecom on 466.075 MHz.
Companies are allowed to use low power paging systems which only cover a single building on several bands including 26.235 MHz to 26.87 MHz and 49 MHz to 49.4875 MHz. Many hospitals have paging systems transmitting between 454.025 MHz and 454.825 MHz.

Until recently it was almost impossible for scanner hobbyists to decode pager messages unless they spent tens of thousands of pounds on equipment designed for the professional surveillance market. But a few years ago an American company Universal Radio Inc. began selling a range of computer controlled and stand alone POCSAG pager decoders. Then last year a British POCSAG decoder known as PD became available for any 286 or above IBM PC compatible. The system consists of a piece of DOS software and a small decoder interface which plugs into a spare serial port on your PC. Full details of how to build the interface (which is dead simple and consists of one integrated circuit and a few other components) come with the program. An evaluation version of the program is available for you to try free of charge. You can get hold of this if you have Internet access by pointing your World Wide Web browser at:-

ftp://ftp.demon.co.uk/pub/ham/scanners

Then download the program "PD-102.ZIP". This is the current version of the software, but it is quite possible by the time you read this a later version will have come out. The evaluation version of PD will only work for a few minutes before stopping but full details of how to get hold of the full version are in the text files which come with the software. With PD running on your computer and the interface connected to you scanner the messages to individual pagers appear on your PC's screen. The full version of PD allows you to save messages sent to certain pagers on disk and allows you to enter a list of pagers whose messages you don't want to be displayed. It can even save an entire days messages to your hard drive.

It now looks however as though POCSAG's days could be numbered. A new European standard system of paging called ERMES (European Radio MEssaging System has been developed and a Europe wide frequency band 169.4 MHz to 169.8 MHz (this is sixteen 25 kHz wide channels) has been allocated. ERMES has several advantages over POCSAG. It uses what is known as four level Frequency Shift Keying modulation which allows data to be sent at 6250 bits a second. Five times faster than using POCSAG. Which means more pagers can use the system and users will notice shorter delays in getting their messages. As all ERMES pagers use the same frequency band and signalling standard it means companies only have to produce one model, unlike the situation at the moment where each country requires a slightly different model. With only one model being produced production costs are lowered and the pagers will be cheaper. One of the best advantages of ERMES however is that if ERMES operators in different countries come to an arrangement then their customers can receive messages on their pager in the other country. The only such agreement at the moment is between a French operator and one in Hungary. But there will soon be lots more of these arrangements. At the moment there are ERMES networks in Cyprus, Denmark, Finland, France, Hungary, the Netherlands, Sweden and Switzerland. Outside Europe networks are being set up in Malaysia and Saudi Arabia so ERMES could soon become a world wide paging standard. However there are problems with ERMES. Tests in Germany found that it caused interference to other radio users. In Britain the frequency band allocated to ERMES is heavily used by handheld radios. At the moment there are no ERMES operators in either country.

It isn't clear at the moment if ERMES uses any form of encryption when sending the users messages over the air to the pager. But if messages are sent in the clear I don't expect it will be long before several ERMES decoders are available for the hobbyist.

With all the coverage in the press about how insecure analogue cellular telephones are I am surprised that there seems to have been no mention just how liable pager messages are to eavesdropping.

Trunked Radio Systems   **3**

Many scanner owners are confused when they hear a channel which at first sounds like a normal PMR system with a conversation between two skip lorry drivers. The conversation ends and the channel goes silent, but then the channel comes to life again with another conversation but this time between a car recovery vehicle and its base. If the scanner owner is listening at a busy time of day it will soon appear as though the single channel has at least ten users. The listener may also hear strange burbling noises at the beginning and end of each conversation and wonder what strange repeater is making these noises.

What they are hearing is a trunked system. There is nothing complicated about these systems which were first used in the United States in the 1970's but did not arrive in Britain until the 1980's. They were introduced because of the vast number of new PMR systems meant that the number of available frequencies was rapidly running out. The problem was that if a frequency was allocated to a car recovery company then even though that companies drivers did not use their radios very often that same frequency could not be allocated to another user in the same area.

Trunking solves this problem by allowing the companies who use the system to be able to use any of a number of channels the system has allocated to it. This is possible because each mobile radio has a small computer built into it. Each of these computers can talk to a central computer located at the radio repeater site. These computers communicate with each other on a special channel allocated to the system known as the control channel, and it is easily recognisable by the constant computer signalling tones which make a burbling noise.

The best way to describe how a trunked system works is by example. Say the Acme Radio Communications Ltd own a small trunked system to serve a city the system is allocated the following frequencies . These are the repeater output frequencies which the mobiles listen to. The mobiles actually transmit 8 MHz lower than the repeater output frequencies.

> 201.8750 MHz Control channel
> 201.4000 MHz Voice channel #1
> 201.4750 MHz Voice channel #2
> 201.5250 MHz Voice channel #3

The system is used by 7 companies:-

> ABC Deliveries
> Hills Pet Taxis
> Smiths Skips
> Harris Farm Supplies
> The Newtown Plumbing Company
> Kings TV Rentals

Roberts Rapid Couriers

At nine in the morning Steve a driver with ABC Deliveries finds his truck has broken down and needs to get in contact with his base. Each unit from each company is allocated an identity number. Steve knows his bases code number is 00 so he enters this into a keypad on his radio and pushes the press to talk (PTT) button on the radio's microphone. At this point the computer in Steve's radio signals via the control channel to the systems control computer that it wishes to talk to ABC Deliveries unit 00. The control computer then sends a message over the control channel asking if ABC Deliveries unit 00 is listening. The computer in the ABC Deliveries base radio hears this and signals back that it is listening. The central computer then searches for an unused voice channel and finds that voice Channel 1 is free. The central computer then signals to Steve's radio and the bases radio to switch to voice Channel 1 and turn on the sets speakers. All of this happens in the fraction of a second between Steve pressing the PTT button and starting to speak. As Steve explains his problem to base the base radio displays Steve's code number 07 on its display. So the people at the base dispatch office know instantly who they are talking to. At the same time Dave, another driver with the company becomes stuck in a traffic jam. He knows that Pete, another driver, will be heading this way soon and wants to warn him about the traffic conditions. Dave knows Pete's code number is 03 so enters this into his keypad and pushes the PTT button. The central computer works as before but finds that as voice Channel 1 is busy, so it tells both mobile radios to go to voice Channel 2 where they talk. If ABC deliveries where using a standard repeater Dave's conversation with Pete would not have been possible as the single channel was already being used by Steve to talk to base, but a trunked system is far more flexible.

While these two conversations are going on Newtown Plumbers receive a phone call from a local factory who's water tank has burst causing major problems. The company decides this is a major job and it needs three plumbers to fix it. The trouble is the plumbers chosen for the repair Mike, John and Julie are already driving to other jobs, but this is no problem for a trunked system at the plumbers base the code numbers for all three plumbers are entered into the office radio and the PTT button pressed. The systems central computers finds that Voice Channel 3 is free so signals to Mike, John and Julie's radios to go to that channel along with Newtown Plumbers base. Then the base is able to talk to all the three plumbers, but the conversation cannot be heard on the other plumbers radios so they are not disturbed while they drive.

Now, by some strange coincidence, Kings TV Rental base needs to get in touch with one of its engineers. His code is entered into the base radio and the PTT button pressed. The system computer searches for a free voice channel, but finds they are all busy so it indicates this to Kings TV base radio. If the base wishes it the system computer waits until a voice channel is free then signals to the Kings TV base and their engineers radio that this is so, and tells them which free voice channel to use. Another advantage of a trunked system is that for example if one of Smiths Skips drivers sees an accident he tries to contact his base so they can call the emergency services, but no voice channels are free. Now the driver presses the EMERGENCY button on his radio, and the mobile radios computer signals to the central computer that this call is an emergency. The central computer then clears a voice channel by signalling to both radios in the conversation to stop transmitting and return to the control channel. The Smiths Skip driver's radio and the bases radio are then signalled to go to that clear voice channel. Each trunked mobile radio also has a unique identity number stored within its computer chips which the radios owner is not able to alter. This is to stop unauthorised radios being used on a network. As at any time the system computer can ask any mobile to send its identity number. The networks owners know the identity number of each radio allowed to use the system and messages from unauthorised ones can be disregarded. This can also be done if an operator has a radio stolen. It is impossible to alter the radios identity number as the chip containing the number is no only soldered to the circuit board it is also glued with epoxy resin making its removal impossible. Trunked systems can be customised to the users demands. Above you will have noticed that ABC Deliveries drivers are able to talk to not only their base but one another. The owner of Harris Farm Supplies thought this would encourage his staff to spend all day chatting to one another, so their mobile radios are only able to talk to base. As soon as they press the PTT button the radios computer knows they can only talk to base and signals this to the systems computer. The owner of Roberts Rapid Couriers however frequently needs to ask which of his vans was closest to a particular location for a pick up, so all his mobile radios had to hear every transmission. All of his firms radios were programmed so that if the PTT button was pressed the radios computer would signal to the systems computers that all Roberts Rapid Couriers radios should be alerted and be sent to the same voice channel to hear the following transmission.

You will have noticed from my above example that the number of companies using the system exceeds the number of channels available. The number of companies using a system depends on the following factors :-
    1) The number of voice channels available, the more available the more conversations can take place at the same time.
    2) How often each company using the system use their radios. A company such as a large delivery firm will use their radios very frequently, and if a number of such companies are put on a network it will become clogged very quickly. A small TV servicing firm is unlikely to use their

radios very often so it possible to put many of these companies onto a network. In reality a trunked system usually includes a mixture of a small number of heavy radio users and a larger number of light users. Security firms are another kind of company who make frequent use of their radios but as they mostly operate at night they can be put on the same system as another heavy radio user such as a large delivery firm who usually only work in the day time.

3) The more companies who use a trunked network the more the radio company who own the network earn. Some radio companies try and increase their earnings by cramming their network with more users than it is capable of taking. This only earns more money for a short period of time as voice channels become crammed and the time users wait before a channel becomes available becomes longer and longer. When this happens the users companies complain and very soon switch to another network.

Although trunked networks sound very complicated they can be monitored by any scanner owner. It is more difficult than listening to old fashioned repeaters, but just take a little more concentration. The best place to hear trunked networks is in area of the radio spectrum known as Band Three. The outputs of the trunked repeaters can be found between:-

176.5 MHz and 183.5 MHz known as Sub Band

One. Where mobile radios transmit 8 MHz higher between 184.5 MHz and 191.5 MHz. also 200.5 MHz and 207.5 MHz known as Sub Band Two. With mobile radios transmitting 8 MHz lower between 192.5 MHz and 199.5 MHz.

The Philips PRM 80 range of trunked mobile radios
Photo courtesy of Philips Telecom

Probably the best band to search is between 200.500 MHz and 207.500 MHz. If you listen you will hear two kinds of signals. The constant burbling of computer data on the control channels and conversations taking place on other channels. Beware though these channels may not be a trunked systems voice channels as this area of the radio spectrum is also allocated to bus companies. Some of the larger bus companies have their own trunked systems but most use old fashioned repeaters. These are recognisable by the absence of computer signalling at the start and end of every conversation. Three large companies

National Band 3 , Wavelength and Radionet operate almost nation-wide Band Three trunked networks which most scanner owners should be able to hear. These companies offer users who require it nation-wide coverage so a company in Leeds will still be able to communicate with a company delivery van in Oxford. A number of smaller regional trunked networks are run by companies like Zycall which covers the Midlands, Mercantile Radio operates a 30 channel system within the M25, Wessex Radio Networks covers Berkshire and Hampshire while Signatel operates in Scotland. The most frequent users of these networks seem to be delivery trucks and as callsigns don't have to be used on a trunked systems, voice channels frequently sound like CB channels!

One other national trunked network is run by Railtrack it is the only user and does not sell time on its network to other companies. The system is complex and allows any train driver with a radio in his cab to call any telephone in the Railtrack internal telephone system. Their network is allocated the following frequencies:-

```
204.8500 MHz Voice channel
204.9000 MHz Voice channel
204.9500 MHz Voice channel
205.0000 MHz Voice channel
205.0500 MHz Voice channel
205.1000 MHz Voice channel
205.1500 MHz Voice channel
205.2000 MHz Voice channel
205.2500 MHz Voice channel
205.3000 MHz Voice channel
205.3500 MHz Voice channel
```

205.4000 MHz Voice channel
205.6000 MHz Voice channel
205.6500 MHz Voice channel
205.6750 MHz Emergency voice channel
205.7000 MHz Voice channel
205.7250 MHz Control channel
205.7500 MHz Voice channel
205.8000 MHz Voice channel
205.8375 MHz Control channel
205.8500 MHz Voice channel
205.9000 MHz Voice channel
206.0000 MHz Voice channel
206.1000 MHz Control channel
206.1500 MHz Voice channel
206.2500 MHz Control channel
206.3000 MHz Voice channel

These frequencies are those transmitted by the trunked base stations the trains transmit on these frequencies minus 8 MHz.
Don't be surprised if you hear the speaking clock while monitoring the voice channels on this network. I have been told that train drivers frequently ring this number on their cab radio to find out if they are on time!

The best way to identify the voice channels of the individual trunked systems is to listen for a distinctive user company perhaps one which gives its callsign or has a base dispatcher with an unusual accent. Then every time you hear this write down the frequency which it is on. To save time as you identify each voice channel lock the frequency out of your scanners search range. Then if you ever hear a user you wish to listen to further you can check the frequency you heard them on against the lists of voice channels you built up earlier. You can then program that systems voice channels into your scanners memories and scan those. Although this is tedious as you will have to press the MEMORY SCAN CONTINUE or CONTINUE button on your scanner every time you hear the other companies on the system. Trunked systems are now popping up all over the radio spectrum other places to search for them are :-

■   In France the best place to find trunked systems is between
34.825 MHz and 36.2 MHz. 85 MHz and 87.5 MHz

■   Water companies have trunked systems here. Most voice channels can be found between 85 MHz and 85.6 MHz while the control channels tend to be between 86.7 MHz and 87 MHz.

■   The R.A.C operate a nation-wide trunked system which can transmit both voice and data. The data is printed out on a small printer in the recovery vehicles cab. The system operates on these frequencies :-

86.4625 MHz	86.5875 MHz	86.6875 MHz
87.0000 MHz	87.0125 MHz	87.0250 MHz
87.0375 MHz	87.0500 MHz	

■   British Gas have a nation-wide trunked system which can be found between 140.0 MHz and 140.5 MHz.

■   The British electricity companies each have their own trunked systems between 139.5 MHz and 140.0 MHz.

■   Securicor is another company which operate their own national trunked network. This can be found on the following frequencies:-

165.8625 MHz	165.8750 MHz	165.8875 MHz
165.9125 MHz	165.9375 MHz	165.9625 MHz
165.9875 MHz		

■   In Germany a national network known as Chekker and owned by German Telecom operates between 420 - 428 MHz (base stations) and 410 - 418 MHz (mobiles).

It seems certain that as the radio spectrum becomes under pressure from more and more users that soon most PMR users will be using trunked networks rather than the old fashioned repeaters which most of them use at the moment. Trunked networks will probably soon be found on nearly all current PMR bands.

Until 1996 the only users of trunked radio systems in Britain were private companies. The situation is very different in the United States where the emergency services of most large cities use these systems. The first of these was the city of Miami which turned on its system in 1985. However the first British public service the Metropolitan Police in London began testing their system in early 1996 and plan to have it fully operational by 1997. This system is different from the previous trunked networks described already which are known as MPT 1327 systems. The Metropolitan Police's system is made by Motorola and is known as SmartZone. SmartZone systems can be recognised because their control channels sound very different from MPT 1327 ones as SmartZone control channels are sending computer data at 3600 bits a second (which makes is sound rather like a high pitched buzz) where as MPT 1327 sends data at only 1200 bits a second and sounds slightly more tuneful. This faster data rate allows SmartZone to do something that is a real pain in the behind for scanner owners. Where as MPT 1327 remains on a single voice channel through-out a conversation I am afraid SmartZone can change frequency every time a Police officer presses his push to talk (PTT) button. To show you what this means imagine a scanner owner who has all the frequencies used by the system in his scanner. Suddenly it stops scanning on 450.9875 MHz and he hears

"Echo control to Hotel 5 attend the 'Smithy Arms' 5 the High Street, intruders on premises"
As soon as Hotel 5 presses his PTT to talk the conversation will move to a different frequency. Now our scanner owner has to search through all the possible frequencies used by the system ignoring all the other conversations on the system to find Hotel 5's response to his control room. If this wasn't difficult enough SmartZone can be made to make a noise (perhaps a little tune) on a frequency after a conversation has just moved to another frequency. This means that once a conversation has changed frequency your scanner will not immediately begin to search for the frequency where the conversation has gone to. Instead the scanner will remain on the channel while the noise continues for a few seconds. Unless you quickly press the

SCAN CONTINUE button on your scanner you may miss the end of the conversation you were following.

There are ways of making monitoring this kind of system slightly easier however. The first thing to do is to use your scanner to search between 450 MHz and 453 MHz in 12.5 kHz steps (not the usual 25 KHz steps used in this band.) Carry out this search on a day and a time when the users of the system are busy and will be using their radios a great deal so that all possible voice channels are used. In the case of the emergency services probably the best time for such a search would be after the pubs close on a Friday or Saturday night. During the search which should last for at least a couple of hours write down the frequencies of any voice channels you find as well as those of any control channels you find. Once you have completed the search enter all the voice frequencies into your scanners memory banks. Now comes the boring part spend at least a night listening to each frequency. If the officers using the frequency give their location then write this down. At the end of the night look at all the locations you have written down you will see that all the locations are in one or two parts of the city. These locations will be geographic such as the north west of the city rather than actual police divisions. Now write down next to the frequency the part or parts of the city the frequency is used in. Then repeat this procedure on every voice frequency you have found. At the end of this exercise you should have found the pool of frequencies which can be used by officers in different parts of the city. Lets say you live in the north east of the city and like to listen to the police in your local area. Look on your list for all frequencies used in the north east (there could be around six) and enter only those into your scanners memories. Although some of these frequencies could also be used in other parts of the city as well. You will have reduced the number of channels you have to scan through for local activity from at least twenty to six. While this won't make monitoring as easy as it used to be in the old days when you only had to monitor one frequency it will make things slightly less difficult. The reason why you must also note down the frequency of the control channels is that unlike MPT 1327 systems where the control channel almost never changes frequency. SmartZone systems can be programmed to frequently change control channel frequency. So every day check the frequency where the control channel was as it might have become a voice channel. Likewise a frequency which was a voice channel might have become a control channel.

Scanner users in the United States have developed a rather more advanced methods of monitoring trunked systems however. They took advantage of the fact that in the USA the Motorola SmartZone trunking system is also used by a large number of private companies. This means that every year as radios are replaced and some companies go bankrupt, a number of SmartZone radios such as the Motorola MTX and the Motorola Saber series of radios are sold on the second hand market (often at gatherings of Radio Hams). Once such a radio has been bought the computer in it has be reprogrammed so that it receives the trunked system you want to monitor. The radios are reprogrammed by connecting them to a PC with a special cable and running some special software from Motorola. It is this that is the problem. Motorola will only sell this software to authorised radio dealers and not to private individuals. The dealers with the software are not allowed to re-sell the software by Motorola. However by various means illegal copies of this software and details of the cable seem to be available in the USA. With the software the cable and some technical information about the set-up of the network it is possible for an interested monitor to program a radio so that it monitors the systems control channel and which then changes frequency to follow the conversations of which ever "talk group" it has been programmed to follow. Talk group is the phrase used to describe a group of users who need to talk to each other. For instance if a police officer calls for assistance then every one with radios in his division needs to hear, but not everyone in his force. In London for example each police division will have its own talk group and each special squad will also have its own talk group. This ability to change frequency and monitor a talk group makes monitoring a trunked user just as easy as monitoring a single frequency on a scanner. Getting hold of the technical information about the network has forced some American monitors to do some very strange things. One author of scanning books in Florida was discovered one night inside a rubbish skip behind a Motorola factory in Miami searching for technical documents that had been thrown away (something known in the USA as dumpster diving). The police found he also had a Motorola radio programmed to follow their talk group. As a result of this he is spending time in a Federal prison. In Tulsa a man was sentenced to years in prison for re-programming radios for members of the press so they could monitor the local police system. He appealed however and was found not guilty. The police do have another way of stopping this kind of monitoring. This is by making the central computer signal over the control channel to ask each radio monitoring to signal back with its own unique identity number. After each radio has signalled back with is identity code these are printed out and compared with a list of the identity codes of the radios the police department owns. Any identity number that is not on this list (which must belong to a monitor) is then "stunned". This is done by sending a special computer instruction on the control channel addressed only to the rogue radio. When the radio receives this instruction its computer destroys itself by over writing its own programming, making it useless.

Another way of following trunked conversations is to build a computerised device to decode the instructions sent to the radios on the control channel. Using one of these devices you can see on your computer screen when a mobile has been sent to a voice channel and tune your scanner to that frequency. So far though no such device has been designed for use by hobbyists.

MPT 1327 and SmartZone aren't the only kinds of trunking systems. The Swedish company Ericsson sells its own system known as EDACS which has sold well both in the USA and Europe. The American company Selectone have a system called SmarTrunk that has been sold all over the world.

With more and more pressure on the radio spectrum trunking is a good method of fitting lots of users efficiently into it. We are bound to see many more trunked systems in the years to come. But don't worry if something you like to monitor starts to use a trunked system it isn't the end of the world. Scanning them is just a little bit more difficult but if you use the techniques I have described it isn't impossible.

GSM Mobile Telephones   4

Perhaps the most popular of all the electronic gadgets of the 1990's is the cellular telephone. So many people have them today it is hard to believe that they were only introduced in 1985. Since then advances in electronics have made the phones smaller, lighter and cheaper.

However they soon became a victim of their own success and problems with the system began to appear. The most noticeable of these was congestion of the system especially in major cities where the sheer number of telephones trying to operate in a small area soon overloaded the system. Governments tried to solve the problem by allowing cellular telephones to use more of the radio spectrum. But as the phones continued to sell in larger and larger numbers even this extra radio spectrum became crowded. The second problem was the system's total lack of voice security. Although cellular telephones contain several modern microprocessors these are used only for signalling over the air to the cellular networks base computer to set up telephone calls.

The actual voices of those using the phones are transmitted using frequency modulation or FM which as many scanner owners quickly found out can easily be listened to. However this was not known by the general public until 1992, the year of the famous Dianagate and Camillagate scandals. When scanner owners allegedly sold newspapers recorded telephone conversations which were supposed to involve the Prince and Princess of Wales. These incidents did serve a useful purpose in warning Joe Public that his car telephone might not be as private as he imagined.

Another problem with the current cellular system is that of fraud. Every cellular telephone sold contains a unique identity number known as the ESN (Electronic Serial Number) stored in a memory chip which is connected to the phones computer chip. The telephone transmits the ESN to the network's central computer which then knows to which phone bill to charge the call. The problem is that with the right equipment it is possible to change this number in many cellular telephones on sale today. This has led to a growing trend of criminals stealing telephones which are then reprogrammed with another ESN belonging to an unsuspecting telephone owner. The telephone is then hired out often to drug dealers who use it make free and untraceable phone calls which only end when the person who the stolen ESN belongs to receives a very surprising telephone bill! When this happens the networks central computer is warned that the ESN is no longer valid and so any further calls from the phone are not accepted. But then all the criminals need do is program the phone with yet another stolen ESN and it can make free calls once again.

Stealing an ESN is easy. The criminal doesn't even have to steal a phone or even have to look at it. The problem is that the computer in the mobile phone transmits the ESN to the networks central computer in the clear not encrypted in any way over the systems control channel. All a criminal needs is a piece of electronic test equipment designed for companies who manufacture and repair cellular phones. This decodes all the computer instructions transmitted on the control channel into plain English which is displayed on a computers screen. When a phone makes a call or even when it is first turned on it transmits its ESN. If the control channel is being monitored by criminals the ESN will flash up on their screen. They can then write it down and later program it into another phone.

The favourite place for ESN thieves to set up their equipment is within a few miles of the exit of a road tunnel. This is because when a car with a mobile phone enters a tunnel its computer loses touch with the network. But when it leaves the tunnel the phone once again can hear the network, so the network's central knows who it is, and the phone transmits its ESN. In this way a criminal can find thousands of ESN's like this during one day.

With increasing numbers of European business and holiday travellers the incompatibility between different countries cellular telephone systems became another problem. A British telephone operates around 900 MHz and uses a different digital signalling standard to a Scandinavian telephone which operates around 450 MHz. French police have been known to seize car telephones from British cars as their use is illegal in France where the British cellular phone frequency band is used by their military.

Planning for the new mobile telephone system began in 1982 when a group of European telecommunications authorities formed a group to look into improvements in European cellular radio. The group was called the Groupe Speciale Mobile or GSM which has become the name of the mobile telephone system the group developed. It took the group until 1990 before they agreed a set of standards for the new system.

To solve the problems mentioned the group decided to use what is known as a digital transmission system. The voice radio transmissions you receive on your scanner are what are known as analogue transmissions. In simple terms these systems work because the sound input to the radios microphone is converted to an electrical waveform. This waveform alters the radio frequency waveform output of the radios transmitter slightly. These slight changes in the radio frequency waveform are detected by the receiver and turned back to sound which is heard from the sets speaker.

Scanner Busters 2

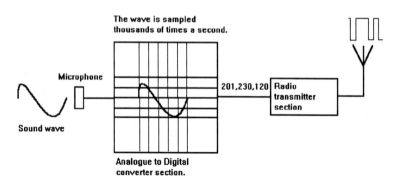

A very basic digital mobile telephone transmitter

A digital transmission system works in a very different way. The sound waveform is still captured by the microphone and turned into an electrical waveform but then this is feed into a chip called an analogue to digital converter. This can be thought of as being similar to a voltage meter with a digital display. It looks at the electrical waveform several thousand times a second (known as the sampling rate) and outputs a number the value of which is dependant on the voltage of the waveform at that particular moment. In this way noises can be represented as numbers.

Computers think of numbers as binary numbers which are numbers which only have two digits one and zero. The number 61 is 0111101 in binary this would be transmitted by a digital transmission system by transmitting a carrier on one frequency to send a zero and transmitting on another frequency a few kilohertz from the other when sending a binary one.

A digital radio receiver takes this binary data from the air and feeds it into a chip called a digital to analogue converter otherwise known as a D to A chip. This works in the opposite way to the A to D chip as it turns the binary numbers back into an analogue electrical wave which the speaker then turns into sound.

It is this digital technology which solves the problems of the old mobile telephones. With the old analogue system there could only be one conversation on each channel at any one time. The GSM system however manages to fit up to eight conversations on one channel by using some very complex technology. The GSM phone samples and measures speech thirteen thousand times a second. During a conversation the phone digitally records speech over a period of 20 milliseconds. The block of numbers representing this speech is then split into eight smaller groups of numbers. Each group is then transmitted with 4.615 milliseconds between each group. It is during this period when the phone is not transmitting that up to seven other telephones can transmit their own small sections of digitised speech. This requires each of the eight phones on the same channel to be perfectly synchronised with the base station otherwise a phone may transmit its digitised speech at the same time as another phone and the resulting clash will mean that sections of both conversations are lost. To stop this each GSM phone has a very accurate clock built into its own small but powerful computer.

GSM mobile telephone data bursts

1 HyperFrame (3Hrs 28Min 53 Secs Long) is made up of 2715648 Frames

1 Frame (0.0004615 Seconds Long)

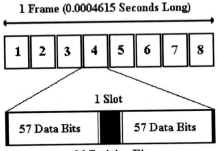

Each frame is made up of 8 slots. These slots can be used to transmit voice information or they can be used to send computer control instructions.

The other side of the conversation is received on another frequency. Again the speech is digitised and again transmitted in small sections in the same way as the mobile telephone transmits to the base station. The main network computer is able to send instructions to the computers in individual phones by using special slots within frames. These instructions could be to tell the phone to change channel as the one it is on has become to busy or it could be to tell a phone that someone is calling it.

In the future it is planned that GSM phones will only sample speech eight thousand times a second rather than the current thirteen thousand times which along with other modifications will mean up to forty conversations on each channel! All of this will be possible without degrading speech quality because of improved computer chips and programs which will be used in the second generation of GSM telephones.

This digital speech means that if a scanner is used to monitor a GSM phone channel all that will be heard is digital noise similar to what you hear if you put your scanner next to your computer. However a knowledgeable person could design a small dedicated computer which would take the audio output of a scanner tuned to a digital signal and feed it into a digital to analogue converter which would output plain speech.

To prevent this happening GSM takes the digital speech data and encrypts (scrambles) it using a mathematical formula called A5. The actual details of A5 are secret but even so parts of it have been posted on the Internet global computer network. Although A5 is very complex what it actually does isn't to complicated and is shown below.

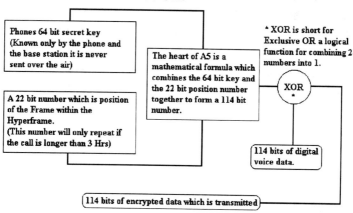

How the GSM A5 encryption system works

A5 is supposed to be very difficult to decode without knowing the 64 bit secret key. This is rumoured to be so difficult that it can't be done quickly even with the powerful super computers belonging to Governments electronic spying agencies such as the NSA in the USA and GCHQ in the UK. For this reason phones using A5 cannot be sold to unfriendly countries. These countries can only be sold phones which use another encryption system known as A5A (Sometimes called A5X) which is much easier and quicker to decode. There are rumours that some European governments would like A5A to be used in Europe as well. They say this would make tapping the calls of drug dealers and terrorists who use GSM phones easier.

To prevent the problem of fraud GSM uses a very interesting system. Each phone has a

A GSM base station antenna. Note the small microwave dish which links the base station to the telephone company's exchange.

small slot in it into which the phones owner must insert a "smart card" before the telephone can make a call. Smart cards are the same size and shape as your bank or credit card but has a computer with its own memory containing information about the telephone user. So far it is impossible to copy smart cards or alter their contents. If a person wants to become a GSM user he first registers with the company who run the phone system they will then be given their own smart card. The user can then buy a telephone from that company or buy one from any local electronics shop. Once he inserts the card he can make telephone calls and they are billed to him. The user could use someone else's telephone but if his smart card is in the slot he will be the one billed for the call at the end of the month. The smart card contains a series of numbers which are only stored in that one card at any point in a conversation the base computer can ask the smart card to send it these numbers over the air if a phone returns wrong numbers the smart card is a fake and the conversation is ended! To prevent someone with very advanced equipment from overseeing these numbers when they are sent over the air they are also encoded. This time with a mathematical formula known as A3.

Another advantage of GSM is that as it is a European standard a GSM phone will soon be able to be used in any of the 12 countries of the European Community. So a British business man will be able to use his car telephone in Berlin and Paris as well as London and all the calls will be billed to his home address. If he wishes to travel light he does not need to take his phone only his smart card which can be carried in a wallet. This can be inserted in any GSM phone any-where in Europe and the call will still be billed back to his home address. In fact now the GSM standard is spreading beyond Europe. Australia's network is about to be launched and several Arab countries have ex-pressed an interest, because of this it has been said that GSM should mean Global System for Mobile com-munications.

The United States of America may be introducing a form of GSM in a few years time. Known as DCS1900 this will operate between 1900 MHz and 2000 MHz. Which will unfortunately make it incompatible the GSM systems in the rest of the world.

In this chapter I have only mentioned the main fea-tures of the GSM system the full specifications drawn up by the GSM committee is more than six thousand pages long. One of the many other features is intended to make a hand portable phones battery last as long as possible. The base station is constantly telling the mobile phone how strong its signals are at the base station. If the signal is very strong the mobile is told to reduce its transmitters output power and so reducing the current being taken from its battery. However if the mobile drives into a valley then the signal strength at the base site will become much weaker so the mobile is to told to increase its transmitters output but when the mobile passes out of the valley then the mobiles output power can be reduced back to normal.

The GSM systems method of what is known as cell handover is also very clever (cell handover is when cellular telephone moves out of the range of one base station and is passed onto another). When a GSM mobile telephone is not receiving or transmitting speech in its timeslots then it is searching the channels assigned for GSM phones to try and find other GSM base stations. When the phone has found 6 other base stations it sends this information plus how strong the signal is from each of the stations to the base station it is currently communicating with. When the base stations detects the signal from the mobile phone is becoming weak it looks at the list of other base stations it has been sent by the phone to find the strongest other base station. It first informs the other base station to prepare to communicate with the phone then tells the mobile phone to change frequency and hand over communications to the other base station. All of this occurs in a thousandth of a second and the persons involved in the telephone call will notice no break in their conversation.

GSM telephones use the following frequencies where the first frequency is the one where the base station transmits and the second is where the mobile phone transmits.

935.20	890.20	GSM Channel 1
935.40	890.40	GSM Channel 2
935.60	890.60	GSM Channel 3
935.80	890.80	GSM Channel 4
936.00	891.00	GSM Channel 5
936.20	891.20	GSM Channel 6
936.40	891.40	GSM Channel 7
936.60	891.60	GSM Channel 8
936.80	891.80	GSM Channel 9
937.00	892.00	GSM Channel 10
937.20	892.20	GSM Channel 11
937.40	892.40	GSM Channel 12
937.60	892.60	GSM Channel 13
937.80	892.80	GSM Channel 14
938.00	893.00	GSM Channel 15
938.20	893.20	GSM Channel 16
938.40	893.40	GSM Channel 17
938.60	893.60	GSM Channel 18
938.80	893.80	GSM Channel 19
939.00	894.00	GSM Channel 20
939.20	894.20	GSM Channel 21
939.40	894.40	GSM Channel 22
939.60	894.60	GSM Channel 23
939.80	894.80	GSM Channel 24
940.00	895.00	GSM Channel 25
940.20	895.20	GSM Channel 26
940.40	895.40	GSM Channel 27
940.60	895.60	GSM Channel 28
940.80	895.80	GSM Channel 29
941.00	896.00	GSM Channel 30
941.20	896.20	GSM Channel 31
941.40	896.40	GSM Channel 32
941.60	896.60	GSM Channel 33
941.80	896.80	GSM Channel 34
942.00	897.00	GSM Channel 35
942.20	897.20	GSM Channel 36

Base	Mobile	
942.40	897.40	GSM Channel 37
942.60	897.60	GSM Channel 38
942.80	897.80	GSM Channel 39
943.00	898.00	GSM Channel 40
943.20	898.20	GSM Channel 41
943.40	898.40	GSM Channel 42
943.60	898.60	GSM Channel 43
943.80	898.80	GSM Channel 44
944.00	899.00	GSM Channel 45
944.20	899.20	GSM Channel 46
944.40	899.40	GSM Channel 47
944.60	899.60	GSM Channel 48
944.80	899.80	GSM Channel 49
945.00	900.00	GSM Channel 50
945.20	900.20	GSM Channel 51
945.40	900.40	GSM Channel 52
945.60	900.60	GSM Channel 53
945.80	900.80	GSM Channel 54
946.00	901.00	GSM Channel 55
946.20	901.20	GSM Channel 56
946.40	901.40	GSM Channel 57
946.60	901.60	GSM Channel 58
946.80	901.80	GSM Channel 59
947.00	902.00	GSM Channel 60
947.20	902.20	GSM Channel 61
947.40	902.40	GSM Channel 62
947.60	902.60	GSM Channel 63
947.80	902.80	GSM Channel 64
948.00	903.00	GSM Channel 65
948.20	903.20	GSM Channel 66
948.40	903.40	GSM Channel 67
948.60	903.60	GSM Channel 68
948.80	903.80	GSM Channel 69
949.00	904.00	GSM Channel 70
949.20	904.20	GSM Channel 71
949.40	904.40	GSM Channel 72
949.60	904.60	GSM Channel 73
949.80	904.80	GSM Channel 74
950.00	905.00	GSM Channel 75
950.20	905.20	GSM Channel 76
950.40	905.40	GSM Channel 77

Scanner Busters *2*

Base	Mobile	
950.60	905.60	GSM Channel 78
950.80	905.80	GSM Channel 79
951.00	906.00	GSM Channel 80
951.20	906.20	GSM Channel 81
951.40	906.40	GSM Channel 82
951.60	906.60	GSM Channel 83
951.80	906.80	GSM Channel 84
952.00	907.00	GSM Channel 85
952.20	907.20	GSM Channel 86
952.40	907.40	GSM Channel 87
952.60	907.60	GSM Channel 88
952.80	907.80	GSM Channel 89
953.00	908.00	GSM Channel 90
953.20	908.20	GSM Channel 91
953.40	908.40	GSM Channel 92
953.60	908.60	GSM Channel 93
953.80	908.80	GSM Channel 94
954.00	909.00	GSM Channel 95
954.20	909.20	GSM Channel 96
954.40	909.40	GSM Channel 97
954.60	909.60	GSM Channel 98
954.80	909.80	GSM Channel 99
955.00	910.00	GSM Channel 100
955.20	910.20	GSM Channel 101
955.40	910.40	GSM Channel 102
955.60	910.60	GSM Channel 103
955.80	910.80	GSM Channel 104
956.00	911.00	GSM Channel 105
956.20	911.20	GSM Channel 106
956.40	911.40	GSM Channel 107
956.60	911.60	GSM Channel 108
956.80	911.80	GSM Channel 109
957.00	912.00	GSM Channel 110
957.20	912.20	GSM Channel 111
957.40	912.40	GSM Channel 112
957.60	912.60	GSM Channel 113
957.80	912.80	GSM Channel 114
958.00	913.00	GSM Channel 115
958.20	913.20	GSM Channel 116
958.40	913.40	GSM Channel 117
958.60	913.60	GSM Channel 118

Base	Mobile	
958.80	913.80	GSM Channel 119
959.00	914.00	GSM Channel 120
959.20	914.20	GSM Channel 121
959.40	914.40	GSM Channel 122
959.60	914.60	GSM Channel 123
959.80	914.80	GSM Channel 124

(All frequencies in MHz)

Currently only Channels 75 to 124 are used for GSM.

Another kind of digital mobile telephone is known as PCN (Personal Communications System) or is sometimes called a DCS 1800 system. These phones work in exactly the same way as GSM phones but use the much higher frequencies listed below. (Where the first frequency is the one where the base station transmits and the second is where the mobile phone transmits.)

1805.00	1710.00	PCS Channel 1
1805.20	1710.20	PCS Channel 2
1805.40	1710.40	PCS Channel 3
1805.60	1710.60	PCS Channel 4
1805.80	1710.80	PCS Channel 5
1806.00	1711.00	PCS Channel 6
1806.20	1711.20	PCS Channel 7
1806.40	1711.40	PCS Channel 8
1806.60	1711.60	PCS Channel 9
1806.80	1711.80	PCS Channel 10
1807.00	1712.00	PCS Channel 11
1807.20	1712.20	PCS Channel 12
1807.40	1712.40	PCS Channel 13
1807.60	1712.60	PCS Channel 14
1807.80	1712.80	PCS Channel 15
1808.00	1713.00	PCS Channel 16
1808.20	1713.20	PCS Channel 17
1808.40	1713.40	PCS Channel 18
1808.60	1713.60	PCS Channel 19
1808.80	1713.80	PCS Channel 20
1809.00	1714.00	PCS Channel 21

Base	Mobile	
1809.20	1714.20	PCS Channel 22
1809.40	1714.40	PCS Channel 23
1809.60	1714.60	PCS Channel 24
1809.80	1714.80	PCS Channel 25
1810.00	1715.00	PCS Channel 26
1810.20	1715.20	PCS Channel 27
1810.40	1715.40	PCS Channel 28
1810.60	1715.60	PCS Channel 29
1810.80	1715.80	PCS Channel 30
1811.00	1716.00	PCS Channel 31
1811.20	1716.20	PCS Channel 32
1811.40	1716.40	PCS Channel 33
1811.60	1716.60	PCS Channel 34
1811.80	1716.80	PCS Channel 35
1812.00	1717.00	PCS Channel 36
1812.20	1717.20	PCS Channel 37
1812.40	1717.40	PCS Channel 38
1812.60	1717.60	PCS Channel 39
1812.80	1717.80	PCS Channel 40
1813.00	1718.00	PCS Channel 41
1813.20	1718.20	PCS Channel 42
1813.40	1718.40	PCS Channel 43
1813.60	1718.60	PCS Channel 44
1813.80	1718.80	PCS Channel 45
1814.00	1719.00	PCS Channel 46
1814.20	1719.20	PCS Channel 47
1814.40	1719.40	PCS Channel 48
1814.60	1719.60	PCS Channel 49
1814.80	1719.80	PCS Channel 50
1815.00	1720.00	PCS Channel 51
1815.20	1720.20	PCS Channel 52
1815.40	1720.40	PCS Channel 53
1815.60	1720.60	PCS Channel 54
1815.80	1720.80	PCS Channel 55
1816.00	1721.00	PCS Channel 56
1816.20	1721.20	PCS Channel 57
1816.40	1721.40	PCS Channel 58
1816.60	1721.60	PCS Channel 59
1816.80	1721.80	PCS Channel 60
1817.00	1722.00	PCS Channel 61
1817.20	1722.20	PCS Channel 62

Base	Mobile	
1817.40	1722.40	PCS Channel 63
1817.60	1722.60	PCS Channel 64
1817.80	1722.80	PCS Channel 65
1818.00	1723.00	PCS Channel 66
1818.20	1723.20	PCS Channel 67
1818.40	1723.40	PCS Channel 68
1818.60	1723.60	PCS Channel 69
1818.80	1723.80	PCS Channel 70
1819.00	1724.00	PCS Channel 71
1819.20	1724.20	PCS Channel 72
1819.40	1724.40	PCS Channel 73
1819.60	1724.60	PCS Channel 74
1819.80	1724.80	PCS Channel 75
1820.00	1725.00	PCS Channel 76
1820.20	1725.20	PCS Channel 77
1820.40	1725.40	PCS Channel 78
1820.60	1725.60	PCS Channel 79
1820.80	1725.80	PCS Channel 80
1821.00	1726.00	PCS Channel 81
1821.20	1726.20	PCS Channel 82
1821.40	1726.40	PCS Channel 83
1821.60	1726.60	PCS Channel 84
1821.80	1726.80	PCS Channel 85
1822.00	1727.00	PCS Channel 86
1822.20	1727.20	PCS Channel 87
1822.40	1727.40	PCS Channel 88
1822.60	1727.60	PCS Channel 89
1822.80	1727.80	PCS Channel 90
1823.00	1728.00	PCS Channel 91
1823.20	1728.20	PCS Channel 92
1823.40	1728.40	PCS Channel 93
1823.60	1728.60	PCS Channel 94
1823.80	1728.80	PCS Channel 95
1824.00	1729.00	PCS Channel 96
1824.20	1729.20	PCS Channel 97
1824.40	1729.40	PCS Channel 98
1824.60	1729.60	PCS Channel 99
1824.80	1729.80	PCS Channel 100
1825.00	1730.00	PCS Channel 101
1825.20	1730.20	PCS Channel 102
1825.40	1730.40	PCS Channel 103

Base	Mobile	
1825.60	1730.60	PCS Channel 104
1825.80	1730.80	PCS Channel 105
1826.00	1731.00	PCS Channel 106
1826.20	1731.20	PCS Channel 107
1826.40	1731.40	PCS Channel 108
1826.60	1731.60	PCS Channel 109
1826.80	1731.80	PCS Channel 110
1827.00	1732.00	PCS Channel 111
1827.20	1732.20	PCS Channel 112
1827.40	1732.40	PCS Channel 113
1827.60	1732.60	PCS Channel 114
1827.80	1732.80	PCS Channel 115
1828.00	1733.00	PCS Channel 116
1828.20	1733.20	PCS Channel 117
1828.40	1733.40	PCS Channel 118
1828.60	1733.60	PCS Channel 119
1828.80	1733.80	PCS Channel 120
1829.00	1734.00	PCS Channel 121
1829.20	1734.20	PCS Channel 122
1829.40	1734.40	PCS Channel 123
1829.60	1734.60	PCS Channel 124
1829.80	1734.80	PCS Channel 125
1830.00	1735.00	PCS Channel 126
1830.20	1735.20	PCS Channel 127
1830.40	1735.40	PCS Channel 128
1830.60	1735.60	PCS Channel 129
1830.80	1735.80	PCS Channel 130
1831.00	1736.00	PCS Channel 131
1831.20	1736.20	PCS Channel 132
1831.40	1736.40	PCS Channel 133
1831.60	1736.60	PCS Channel 134
1831.80	1736.80	PCS Channel 135
1832.00	1737.00	PCS Channel 136
1832.20	1737.20	PCS Channel 137
1832.40	1737.40	PCS Channel 138
1832.60	1737.60	PCS Channel 139
1832.80	1737.80	PCS Channel 140
1833.00	1738.00	PCS Channel 141
1833.20	1738.20	PCS Channel 142
1833.40	1738.40	PCS Channel 143
1833.60	1738.60	PCS Channel 144

Base	Mobile	
1833.80	1738.80	PCS Channel 145
1834.00	1739.00	PCS Channel 146
1834.20	1739.20	PCS Channel 147
1834.40	1739.40	PCS Channel 148
1834.60	1739.60	PCS Channel 149
1834.80	1739.80	PCS Channel 150
1835.00	1740.00	PCS Channel 151
1835.20	1740.20	PCS Channel 152
1835.40	1740.40	PCS Channel 153
1835.60	1740.60	PCS Channel 154
1835.80	1740.80	PCS Channel 155
1836.00	1741.00	PCS Channel 156
1836.20	1741.20	PCS Channel 157
1836.40	1741.40	PCS Channel 158
1836.60	1741.60	PCS Channel 159
1836.80	1741.80	PCS Channel 160
1837.00	1742.00	PCS Channel 161
1837.20	1742.20	PCS Channel 162
1837.40	1742.40	PCS Channel 163
1837.60	1742.60	PCS Channel 164
1837.80	1742.80	PCS Channel 165
1838.00	1743.00	PCS Channel 166
1838.20	1743.20	PCS Channel 167
1838.40	1743.40	PCS Channel 168
1838.60	1743.60	PCS Channel 169
1838.80	1743.80	PCS Channel 170
1839.00	1744.00	PCS Channel 171
1839.20	1744.20	PCS Channel 172
1839.40	1744.40	PCS Channel 173
1839.60	1744.60	PCS Channel 174
1839.80	1744.80	PCS Channel 175
1840.00	1745.00	PCS Channel 176
1840.20	1745.20	PCS Channel 177
1840.40	1745.40	PCS Channel 178
1840.60	1745.60	PCS Channel 179
1840.80	1745.80	PCS Channel 180
1841.00	1746.00	PCS Channel 181
1841.20	1746.20	PCS Channel 182
1841.40	1746.40	PCS Channel 183
1841.60	1746.60	PCS Channel 184
1841.80	1746.80	PCS Channel 185

Scanner Busters 2

Base	Mobile	
1842.00	1747.00	PCS Channel 186
1842.20	1747.20	PCS Channel 187
1842.40	1747.40	PCS Channel 188
1842.60	1747.60	PCS Channel 189
1842.80	1747.80	PCS Channel 190
1843.00	1748.00	PCS Channel 191
1843.20	1748.20	PCS Channel 192
1843.40	1748.40	PCS Channel 193
1843.60	1748.60	PCS Channel 194
1843.80	1748.80	PCS Channel 195
1844.00	1749.00	PCS Channel 196
1844.20	1749.20	PCS Channel 197
1844.40	1749.40	PCS Channel 198
1844.60	1749.60	PCS Channel 199
1844.80	1749.80	PCS Channel 200
1845.00	1750.00	PCS Channel 201
1845.20	1750.20	PCS Channel 202
1845.40	1750.40	PCS Channel 203
1845.60	1750.60	PCS Channel 204
1845.80	1750.80	PCS Channel 205
1846.00	1751.00	PCS Channel 206
1846.20	1751.20	PCS Channel 207
1846.40	1751.40	PCS Channel 208
1846.60	1751.60	PCS Channel 209
1846.80	1751.80	PCS Channel 210
1847.00	1752.00	PCS Channel 211
1847.20	1752.20	PCS Channel 212
1847.40	1752.40	PCS Channel 213
1847.60	1752.60	PCS Channel 214
1847.80	1752.80	PCS Channel 215
1848.00	1753.00	PCS Channel 216
1848.20	1753.20	PCS Channel 217
1848.40	1753.40	PCS Channel 218
1848.60	1753.60	PCS Channel 219
1848.80	1753.80	PCS Channel 220
1849.00	1754.00	PCS Channel 221
1849.20	1754.20	PCS Channel 222
1849.40	1754.40	PCS Channel 223
1849.60	1754.60	PCS Channel 224
1849.80	1754.80	PCS Channel 225
1850.00	1755.00	PCS Channel 226

Base	Mobile	
1850.20	1755.20	PCS Channel 227
1850.40	1755.40	PCS Channel 228
1850.60	1755.60	PCS Channel 229
1850.80	1755.80	PCS Channel 230
1851.00	1756.00	PCS Channel 231
1851.20	1756.20	PCS Channel 232
1851.40	1756.40	PCS Channel 233
1851.60	1756.60	PCS Channel 234
1851.80	1756.80	PCS Channel 235
1852.00	1757.00	PCS Channel 236
1852.20	1757.20	PCS Channel 237
1852.40	1757.40	PCS Channel 238
1852.60	1757.60	PCS Channel 239
1852.80	1757.80	PCS Channel 240
1853.00	1758.00	PCS Channel 241
1853.20	1758.20	PCS Channel 242
1853.40	1758.40	PCS Channel 243
1853.60	1758.60	PCS Channel 244
1853.80	1758.80	PCS Channel 245
1854.00	1759.00	PCS Channel 246
1854.20	1759.20	PCS Channel 247
1854.40	1759.40	PCS Channel 248
1854.60	1759.60	PCS Channel 249
1854.80	1759.80	PCS Channel 250
1855.00	1760.00	PCS Channel 251
1855.20	1760.20	PCS Channel 252
1855.40	1760.40	PCS Channel 253
1855.60	1760.60	PCS Channel 254
1855.80	1760.80	PCS Channel 255
1856.00	1761.00	PCS Channel 256
1856.20	1761.20	PCS Channel 257
1856.40	1761.40	PCS Channel 258
1856.60	1761.60	PCS Channel 259
1856.80	1761.80	PCS Channel 260
1857.00	1762.00	PCS Channel 261
1857.20	1762.20	PCS Channel 262
1857.40	1762.40	PCS Channel 263
1857.60	1762.60	PCS Channel 264
1857.80	1762.80	PCS Channel 265
1858.00	1763.00	PCS Channel 266
1858.20	1763.20	PCS Channel 267

Scanner Busters 2

Base	Mobile		
1858.40	1763.40	PCS Channel	268
1858.60	1763.60	PCS Channel	269
1858.80	1763.80	PCS Channel	270
1859.00	1764.00	PCS Channel	271
1859.20	1764.20	PCS Channel	272
1859.40	1764.40	PCS Channel	273
1859.60	1764.60	PCS Channel	274
1859.80	1764.80	PCS Channel	275
1860.00	1765.00	PCS Channel	276
1860.20	1765.20	PCS Channel	277
1860.40	1765.40	PCS Channel	278
1860.60	1765.60	PCS Channel	279
1860.80	1765.80	PCS Channel	280
1861.00	1766.00	PCS Channel	281
1861.20	1766.20	PCS Channel	282
1861.40	1766.40	PCS Channel	283
1861.60	1766.60	PCS Channel	284
1861.80	1766.80	PCS Channel	285
1862.00	1767.00	PCS Channel	286
1862.20	1767.20	PCS Channel	287
1862.40	1767.40	PCS Channel	288
1862.60	1767.60	PCS Channel	289
1862.80	1767.80	PCS Channel	290
1863.00	1768.00	PCS Channel	291
1863.20	1768.20	PCS Channel	292
1863.40	1768.40	PCS Channel	293
1863.60	1768.60	PCS Channel	294
1863.80	1768.80	PCS Channel	295
1864.00	1769.00	PCS Channel	296
1864.20	1769.20	PCS Channel	297
1864.40	1769.40	PCS Channel	298
1864.60	1769.60	PCS Channel	299
1864.80	1769.80	PCS Channel	300
1865.00	1770.00	PCS Channel	301
1865.20	1770.20	PCS Channel	302
1865.40	1770.40	PCS Channel	303
1865.60	1770.60	PCS Channel	304
1865.80	1770.80	PCS Channel	305
1866.00	1771.00	PCS Channel	306
1866.20	1771.20	PCS Channel	307
1866.40	1771.40	PCS Channel	308

Base	Mobile	
1866.60	1771.60	PCS Channel 309
1866.80	1771.80	PCS Channel 310
1867.00	1772.00	PCS Channel 311
1867.20	1772.20	PCS Channel 312
1867.40	1772.40	PCS Channel 313
1867.60	1772.60	PCS Channel 314
1867.80	1772.80	PCS Channel 315
1868.00	1773.00	PCS Channel 316
1868.20	1773.20	PCS Channel 317
1868.40	1773.40	PCS Channel 318
1868.60	1773.60	PCS Channel 319
1868.80	1773.80	PCS Channel 320
1869.00	1774.00	PCS Channel 321
1869.20	1774.20	PCS Channel 322
1869.40	1774.40	PCS Channel 323
1869.60	1774.60	PCS Channel 324
1869.80	1774.80	PCS Channel 325
1870.00	1775.00	PCS Channel 326
1870.20	1775.20	PCS Channel 327
1870.40	1775.40	PCS Channel 328
1870.60	1775.60	PCS Channel 329
1870.80	1775.80	PCS Channel 330
1871.00	1776.00	PCS Channel 331
1871.20	1776.20	PCS Channel 332
1871.40	1776.40	PCS Channel 333
1871.60	1776.60	PCS Channel 334
1871.80	1776.80	PCS Channel 335
1872.00	1777.00	PCS Channel 336
1872.20	1777.20	PCS Channel 337
1872.40	1777.40	PCS Channel 338
1872.60	1777.60	PCS Channel 339
1872.80	1777.80	PCS Channel 340
1873.00	1778.00	PCS Channel 341
1873.20	1778.20	PCS Channel 342
1873.40	1778.40	PCS Channel 343
1873.60	1778.60	PCS Channel 344
1873.80	1778.80	PCS Channel 345
1874.00	1779.00	PCS Channel 346
1874.20	1779.20	PCS Channel 347
1874.40	1779.40	PCS Channel 348
1874.60	1779.60	PCS Channel 349

Base	Mobile	
1874.80	1779.80	PCS Channel 350
1875.00	1780.00	PCS Channel 351
1875.20	1780.20	PCS Channel 352
1875.40	1780.40	PCS Channel 353
1875.60	1780.60	PCS Channel 354
1875.80	1780.80	PCS Channel 355
1876.00	1781.00	PCS Channel 356
1876.20	1781.20	PCS Channel 357
1876.40	1781.40	PCS Channel 358
1876.60	1781.60	PCS Channel 359
1876.80	1781.80	PCS Channel 360
1877.00	1782.00	PCS Channel 361
1877.20	1782.20	PCS Channel 362
1877.40	1782.40	PCS Channel 363
1877.60	1782.60	PCS Channel 364
1877.80	1782.80	PCS Channel 365
1878.00	1783.00	PCS Channel 366
1878.20	1783.20	PCS Channel 367
1878.40	1783.40	PCS Channel 368
1878.60	1783.60	PCS Channel 369
1878.80	1783.80	PCS Channel 370
1879.00	1784.00	PCS Channel 371
1879.20	1784.20	PCS Channel 372
1879.40	1784.40	PCS Channel 373
1879.60	1784.60	PCS Channel 374

(All frequencies in MHz)

In Britain there are 2 PCS networks Mercury One to One and another called Orange.

You can listen to the digital noises made by GSM telephones on your scanner if you listen to the frequencies bands where the base stations transmit (950 MHz - 960 MHz and 1805 MHz - 1880 MHz) in wide band FM mode. However all you will hear when listening is the sound of a high pitched whistle with a rapid tapping noise in the background. Don't even hope to be able to decode this at the moment.

One interesting way of listening to GSM phones has been found already however. In 1995 the *Sunday Times* of London reported that a company specialising in electronic surveillance devices had offered for sale a computer capable of monitoring GSM calls to its reporters for £20,000.

The device works not by listening to the phone to base station communications on the 900 MHz band but by monitoring the microwave link between a base station and the phone companies central telephone exchange. This link carries all phone conversations being transmitted by the base station and all its computer communications. For this monitoring device to work the base station must have already decrypted the phone conversations using A5 before it is retransmitted on the microwave link which is probably multiplexed (this means that all the phone conversations going on are combined into one signal) but not encrypted.

This method would be very difficult for the hobbyist to use for two reasons. The first is that the microwave links use frequencies of either 23 GHz (23,000 MHz) or 38 GHz (38,000 MHz) and receivers for these frequencies are difficult to get hold of and expensive. The second reason is that the signals from these microwave transmitters are very directional and to be able to monitor them you would have to position your antenna somewhere on a line between the base station and the telephone exchange. Anyway if monitoring phone calls this way did become common all the phone companies would have to do is encrypt the link.

At the moment monitoring GSM phones using the A5 encryption system seems almost impossible. However if in the future governments force the phone companies to use a weaker encryption system and the technical details of this leak. Then GSM phones will be become vulnerable to eavesdropping

If you enjoy monitoring mobile phones there is no need to worry at the moment. Although the number of users on the digital networks will rise, but old analogue phones are still getting cheaper. It is rumoured that in Britain the older analogue networks will probably operate until the year 2005. This will leave hobbyists with plenty to listen to for the next few years.

Digital Cordless Telephones   5

During the early nineteen eighties Europe was being flooded with cordless telephones imported from the Far East. Some of these telephones operated on 46 MHz some on 49 MHz and I remember to my surprise hearing one operating on 70.25 MHz a radio amateurs frequency. Some of the telephones used quite high power transmitters and had a range of several miles while others were only short range. It was not long before the radio authorities of Europe were receiving thousands of complaints about these telephones interfering with PMR and emergency service radios as well as causing interference to TV sets. To stop these problems Europe responded by specifying a set of standards for all European cordless telephones known as CT1. The British decided however that a CT1 standard telephone would be to expensive so designed its own standard. The French did not like the frequencies used in the CT1 standard so French cordless telephones used different ones. So the standard was a failure.

In Britain cordless telephones soon became very popular but there were problems. Only eight channels were allocated and in built up areas these channels quickly filled, and telephones began interfering with others on the same frequency. Because the sys-

tem used narrow band frequency modulation an analogue method conversations on these cordless telephones could be easily be monitored by someone with
a scanner so there was no privacy for the users. For
a second time the governments of Europe brought
together electronics and telecommunications companies to agree on a more advanced standard. While
everyone involved decided the standard had to be
digital as this would give the user more privacy and
better audio quality but also because this would use
less radio spectrum. There were disagreements however on both the frequencies to be used and the digital system involved. Because of this instead of one
standard there are two European cordless telephone
standards. One is DECT (Digital European Cordless
Telecommunications) and the other is known as CT2.
As CT2 was the least complex of the two systems it
was the first to become operational and was allocated
the following frequencies.

```
864.150 MHz channel 01
864.250 MHz channel 02
864.350 MHz channel 03
864.450 MHz channel 04
864.550 MHz channel 05
864.650 MHz channel 06
864.750 MHz channel 07
864.850 MHz channel 08
864.950 MHz channel 09
865.050 MHz channel 10
865.150 MHz channel 11
865.250 MHz channel 12
865.350 MHz channel 13
865.450 MHz channel 14
865.550 MHz channel 15
865.650 MHz channel 16
865.750 MHz channel 17
```

865.850 MHz channel 18
865.950 MHz channel 19
866.050 MHz channel 20
866.150 MHz channel 21
866.250 MHz channel 22
866.350 MHz channel 23
866.450 MHz channel 24
866.550 MHz channel 25
866.650 MHz channel 26
866.750 MHz channel 27
866.850 MHz channel 28
866.950 MHz channel 29
867.050 MHz channel 30
867.150 MHz channel 31
867.250 MHz channel 32
867.350 MHz channel 33
867.450 MHz channel 34
867.550 MHz channel 35
867.650 MHz channel 36
867.750 MHz channel 37
867.850 MHz channel 38
867.950 MHz channel 39
868.050 MHz channel 40

Conversations on a CT2 telephone are what is known as full duplex meaning both people using the telephone can talk and listen at the same time just like an old fashioned landline telephone. Both analogue mobile phones and digital GSM telephones are also full duplex but require two frequencies for each conversation, one for each side of the conversation. However a CT2 phone achieves full a duplex conversation using only one frequency by using a method known as digital ping pong.

When a person speaks into a CT2 phone their voice is sampled by an analogue to digital converter chip thousands of a times a second. The digital values of speech over a period of one thousandth of a second are transmitted one after another. Then the phones transmitter then turns off and the receiver listens on the same frequency as the base transmits digital data for one thousandth of a second. This is then turned back into an analogue wave by a digital to analogue converter chip then outputted by the phones speaker. Then the phones transmitter is turned back on and the next one thousandth of a second digitised speech is transmitted. This switching between receive and transmit on the same frequency takes place so rapidly the telephones user does not notice it. Just like old style cordless phones a CT2 phone can be used in the home along with a small base station connected to the houses telephone line. However a CT2 telephone can be used outside the home as the Department of Trade and Industry allowed several groups of companies to built CT2 base stations all over Britain. So if a person with a CT2 phone was in a city centre and suddenly realised he needed to make a phone call all he would have to do is look for a sign showing a CT2 base station was nearby then once stood within fifty metres of the base he can make his call. However a CT2 telephone can only receive calls when it is within range of its home base station and cannot receive call from public base stations on the street.

As these public base stations only have a range of fifty metres to give decent coverage of Britain's built up areas many thousands of them needed to be built and fitted to buildings costing the companies involved millions of Pounds. However possibly because of the inability to receive calls the number of CT2 phones sold was very small. Soon all but one of the companies involved with the project dropped out. The remaining company was Hutchinson telecom who launched their CT2 network called RABBIT with a great deal of advertising in northern England. Their public base stations identified with a small blue sign with a Rabbits head on it can be found in many motorway service stations and above shops near city centres all over Britain. But despite the extensive advertisements and thousands of base stations all over the country RABBIT failed to capture the publics imagination. The network closed in December 1993 by the spring of 1994 most of the public base stations seem to have been removed.

The CT2 system is still being sold to companies as an ideal way of keeping in touch with it employees anywhere in the companies offices or factory. Employees of the Tyne tunnel in northern England use CT2 phones to keep in touch and make sure the traffic keeps flowing. The South Staffordshire water company has replaced its emergency PMR system with a multi base CT2 system. The system is also becoming popular abroad. In France where the local CT2 phone system is called Bi-Bop by its owners French Telecom. Also in Asia Hong Kong has a popular system and other countries such as China and Vietnam are about to build networks.

DECT is similar to CT2 as it also uses digital ping pong to fit both sides of a conversation onto one frequency. DECT is more advanced though as it can fit up to twelve telephone conversations onto one frequency compared to CT2 which is limited to one conversation on each frequency. DECT does this in a very similar way to GSM. Each telephone is told by its base station when it is allowed to transmit. The phone then transmits a small section of its digitised speech. When it stops other phones on the same frequency can transmit their sections of speech one after another. After all the phones have transmitted the base station

An Alcatel 4075 DECT mobile telephone. Photo courtesy of Alcatel.

transmits small sections of the other sides of the conversations to each of the phones in turn. If a DECT user talking on his phone walks out of the range of one base station his phone is able to search for another base station and if it finds one it can transfer the call to that base station. Something a CT2 telephone is unable to do. DECT phones have been on sale now for around a year. Perhaps because they are more expensive than the cheap analogue phones the companies selling them are not aiming them at the consumer but at other companies instead. So far they have been sold to large companies for use in their headquarters offices but also these phones have also been sold to small garden centres. Companies are prepared to pay more for these phones because they offer clearer reception and greater range than cheaper cordless ones.

In Europe the following ten channels have been allocated for use by DECT phones.

1881.792 MHz channel 1
1883.520 MHz channel 2
1885.248 MHz channel 3
1886.976 MHz channel 4
1888.704 MHz channel 5
1890.432 MHz channel 6
1892.160 MHz channel 7
1893.888 MHz channel 8
1895.616 MHz channel 9
1897.344 MHz channel 10

It is impossible to eavesdrop on a CT2 or DECT telephone conversation with any radio scanner available today. If you do tune to one of these frequencies I have listed when a call is in progress all you will hear is the buzzing noise of the digital ping pong. Unlike GSM however CT2 and DECT do not encode their digitised voice transmissions. So perhaps it is possible for a very clever scanner hobbyist to built a circuit which would turn the digital ping pong transmissions back into sound. However because the maximum power of a CT2 and DECT phones is only 10mW any scanner receiving them would have to be within one hundred metres of the phone and base station making eavesdropping difficult.

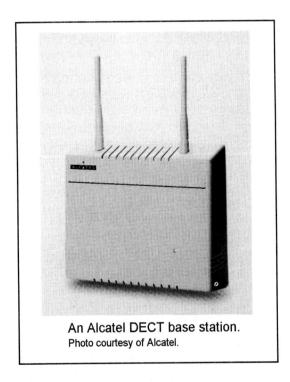

An Alcatel DECT base station.
Photo courtesy of Alcatel.

Spread Spectrum   **6**

Most of the new radio systems I have described try to fit more users into the radio spectrum by reducing the amount of radio spectrum each radio uses. The spread spectrum system however tries to fit more users into the radio spectrum by allowing each radio to use a larger part of the spectrum. There are several kinds of spread spectrum. One is Chirp in this method the carrier frequency of a transmitter is made to rapidly sweep backwards and forwards across part of the radio spectrum. Another is known as direct sequence spread spectrum. A narrow band radio transmission concentrates all of its radio energy within a few kilohertz of the radio spectrum. But direct sequence spread spectrum system spreads the signal and dilutes the radio energy across several megahertz of the spectrum. The radio energy is spread so much that the signal is only just above the noise which is always present in the radio spectrum. This makes a direct sequence spread spectrum transmission impossible to monitor on a narrow band receiver such as a scanner and also very difficult to even detect without a sensitive spectrum analyser. But the most frequently used kind of spread spectrum is frequency hopping. This is just what its name suggests the radio transmitter involved changes its transmitting frequency several times a second. Which means any receivers must know the exact sequence of frequencies the transmitter will use. Obviously there are tens of billions of these sequences making this form of spread spectrum impossible for someone who does not know the sequence of frequencies to monitor.

Due to this and because a signal using this method of transmission would be very difficult to jam and to locate by radio direction finding that frequency hopping spread spectrum radios were developed for and are mainly used by the military, who first started to use it during the late 1940's. Then a spread spectrum transceiver would take up an entire room, but now the British army uses radios such as the Racal Jaguar-V, a backpack radio. This radio can transmit or receive on any frequency between 30 MHz and 88 MHz and can change frequency up to 200 times a second. Not only does it frequency hop but in case the enemy manages to work out the hopping system it also digitises and scrambles the speech it transmits. Racal also sell the Caracal the worlds first digitally scrambled frequency hopping handheld radio which weighs less than one kilogram. In the late 1980's the US army and Marine corps introduced a new range of radios named SINCGARS (Single Channel Ground and Airborne Radio System). This is a range of radios based around the AN/PRC-119 manpack radio and the ITT AN/PRC-201. All SINCGARS radios are frequency hoppers able to change frequency around 100 times a second on any frequency between 30 MHz and 88 MHz with 25 kHz channel spacing. Very soon these will be the most numerous radios in the US army. The army is not the only of the armed services to use spread spectrum. In 1980 the US Air Force began a program called HAVE QUICK the aim of which was to obtain jam proof and secure radios for USAF aircraft. One radio developed for the program was the AN/ARC-164 airborne radio by the Magnavox government and electronics company of Indiana. Between 1980 and 1987 the USAF spent approximately $60 million equipping its aircraft with these radios. In the United States scanner owners have heard HAVE QUICK radios in use hopping between 5 or more UHF airband frequencies. They have claimed it is possible to monitor some of the HAVE QUICK transmissions by listening to several scanners at once with each scanner having a few of the frequencies in its memories. As they increased the number of scanners used for this the conversations became less choppy sounding. In

HAVE QUICK II radios had to be quickly fitted to RAF Buccaneer aircraft during the Gulf War.

1987 development of a more advanced version of the radio known as HAVE QUICK II began. One buyer of HAVE QUICK II radios was the RAF. Some of them had to be quickly fitted to the Buccaneer aircraft sent to the Gulf War to be used as laser designators (this is an aircraft which points a laser beam at a target other aircraft then drop laser guided bombs which follow this beam). So it is likely that the other RAF aircraft out in the Gulf were already were fitted with HAVE QUICK II radios. Until 1995 there were few reports of HAVE QUICK II radios being used, but this has now all changed the AWACS radar control aircraft of the US Air Force, RAF and multi national NATO force (the aircraft tend to use the callsigns NATO and MAGIC) use HAVE QUICK II to communicate with the fighters they are controlling. Monitors have reported that another regular HAVE QUICK II user are the US Air Force F15 strike eagles of the 48 Tactical Fighter Wing based at RAF Lakenheath. The following frequencies have been noted with HAVE QUICK II activity:-

231.350 MHz	232.150 MHz	240.400 MHz
245.725 MHz	246.950 MHz	252.925 MHz
254.450 MHz	263.325 MHz	263.575 MHz
264.500 MHz	276.425 MHz	278.425 MHz
283.850 MHz	283.875 MHz	291.250 MHz
292.425 MHz	300.725 MHz	306.500 MHz
308.550 MHz	310.075 MHz	310.900 MHz
312.925 MHz	316.550 MHz	328.400 MHz
337.025 MHz	338.950 MHz	339.425 MHz
344.925 MHz	357.325 MHz	359.350 MHz
366.825 MHz	372.450 MHz	374.425 MHz
380.650 MHz	381.225 MHz	385.150 MHz
385.225 MHz	385.525 MHz	399.450 MHz

So although most military aircraft will soon be fitted with HAVE QUICK radios I don't think the frequency hopping option will be used for much normal peace time use. There are problems with frequency hopping which make it inappropriate to use in safety critical messages such as air traffic control where one missed message could mean disaster, but we will see its increased use for tactical messages during exercises.

The problem with changing frequency very quickly is that if a receivers computers clock does not keep time exactly with the clock in the transmitters computer the receiver will listen on frequencies at the wrong time so communication is lost. This is known as a synchronisation error, and some American listeners discovered when this happens some government spread spectrum radios stopped hopping. They went to one frequency where plain voice communication took place before the computers in the radios were synchronised and hopping begins again. The military usually programs its radio to use otherwise unused frequencies for this purpose, but some American scanner owners have claimed to hear these transmissions.

One approach the military use to monitoring spread spectrum signals is known as the wide band sharp beam system. If one army discovers another army is using a spread spectrum radio system which is frequency hopping between 40 MHz and 50 MHz. Then a standard communications receiver would be modified so that its receive bandwidth is altered from the usual 10 KHz or 100 KHz to 10 MHz. This means that is the receiver is tuned to 45 MHz it will be able to receive any transmission between 40 MHz and 50 MHz. If this receiver is connected to a sharp beam antenna (one which only receives signals transmitted from the direction the antenna is pointing and not from other directions) then the frequency hopping conversations can be monitored. If a sharp beam antenna wasn't used then the wideband receiver would monitor every transmission taking place between 40 MHz and 50 MHz and the frequency hopping signal would be lost in the clutter of other signals. Of course now most military spread spectrum systems also scramble the voice transmissions.

In the last few years though spread spectrum has started to be used by other groups. Radio amateurs will soon be allowed to use the mode and plans for spread spectrum transceivers have started to appear in electronics magazines. This is because using spread spectrum allows more users to transmit in part of the radio spectrum than would be able to use it if they were using more normal transmission systems. As spread spectrum literally spreads a transmission over a frequency band the power of the transmission is diluted across the band. If this frequency band is wide enough this dilution means the power on any one frequency is hardly noticeable. So the frequencies can be used by other users.

The first commercial users of spread spectrum systems have been medium size computer networks. The usual way of connecting computers together in offices has been with coaxial cable but as each computer needs a cable the office can quickly become full of cables. These can be tied up and put in conduits but this then makes re-arranging the office or even adding a new computer to the network a lengthy job.

What was needed was a wireless network however a normal radio transmitter would be no good because the data needs to be sent at a very high speed and megahertz of bandwidth would be required by each network. So any spectrum made available for such a system would be quickly filled. An infra red system was tried but each computer had to be within sight of the central infra red transceiver. If a filling cabinet was moved into this path or if someone stood in the way then the link would be lost.

Some companies are developing spread spectrum links as the answer to these problems as its wide bandwidth allows high speed data communication and because it is an efficient use of the radio spectrum. Small circuit boards containing the radio equipment plug into each computer and a tiny antenna pokes out of the back of the computer's case. Another antenna is mounted on the computer room's ceiling. This belongs to the networks central computer which communicates with all the other computers in the room.

At the moment there are several different kinds of these networks all use the microwave part of the radio spectrum usually in the 2.4 GHz region. Microwaves are used because they cannot pass through walls. This limits the range of a system to a few rooms which allows many of these networks to be used in a small areas such as a city centre full of office buildings.

A few of the spread spectrum computer wireless networks are already being used in Britain, but European standard data signalling systems and frequency bands are now just being decided by governments. When these standards are decided then wireless networks will become more widespread then they could very quickly attract a new form of computer cracker who equipped with a wideband receiver and a computer tries to steal software and data from companies using them. This would be possible if the receiver was close to the network or used a very high gain narrow beam microwave dish antenna to amplify the signal and if the data being sent to the computers was not encoded. To prevent this wireless network manufacturers will have to make sure their systems use a very secure method of encoding the data.

At the moment there are no plans for the emergency services or private companies to use spread spectrum for voice communications, but as technology advances and the radio spectrum more crowded it may be possible in the future.

Voice Scrambling Systems   7

While perhaps 99% of people who buy scanners use them either as part of a hobby (such as aircraft enthusiasts) or use them in listen to the emergency services in their local area. I don't think this is a particularly bad thing, many hobbyists I have spoken to say that until they listened to their local police they didn't realise how undermanned they are and how dangerous the job. I also know hobbyists who have seen criminal suspects and stolen cars after hearing details of them being passed on the police channels and have then phoned the police to tell them what they have seen. We have to except however that scanners can have there dark side. In the North of England Ramraiders (thieves who steal a car then use it to crash through the front of a shop so they can steal its merchandise) will use scanners to find out if they have been spotted by the police. Flying squad officers in London have found that when they arrest an armed robber not only does he have a gun but he often has a scanner. As listening to the police is illegal in Britain the police first tried various sting operations to catch scanner owners. In Warrington the police announced on their main radio channel that a UFO had been seen landing in a field of course anyone stupid enough to turn up and have a look was arrested. South Yorkshire police tried the same trick with their Operation Marconi one day telling officers a UFO had landed and the next announcing that a bag of money had burst and ten pound notes were blowing all over a field. The trouble with these kind of operations is that it tends to be curious teenagers that are caught rather than hardened criminals.

Of course the best way to protect your voice communications against eavesdroppers is not to rely on outdated and unenforceable laws against scanners but to use voice encryption (scrambling) systems. The first of these systems to be commonly used is known as "Voice Inversion scrambling" this works by changing the audio frequencies in the human voice around. High frequencies are turned into low frequencies and low ones into high frequencies. This has the effect of making a man sound rather like Donald Duck. The problem is that it is very easy to descramble this system by the following means.

1   With a simple electronic circuit these can be bought from Ramsey electronics in the USA.

2   There are programs which use an IBM PC compatible computer and soundcard to do the same thing.

3   Or if your scanner can receive single side band modulation (such as the AOR3000) tune into a voice inversion signal then try switching to USB or LSB (or turn the BFO knob if your receiver has one) and this will descramble the signal.

Voice inversion scrambling is still used by a few American police departments and by some analogue cordless phones but scrambling technology has now moved on.

One such system is sold by the British company Marconi its name is MASC (Marconi Advanced SCrambler). MASC consists of a small circuit board which can be fitted in new handheld radios when they are manufactured (such as the Philips PRP74) or can be fitted into existing police radios such as the Philips PFX, Motorola HT600 or Kenwood TK340. MASC uses a form of encryption known as band scrambling. This takes a section of human speech and splits it into bands of frequencies (e.g. 300 Hz - 400 Hz, 400 Hz - 500 Hz and so on) then it re-arranges the order of these bands. So that any frequencies in the range 800 Hz - 900 Hz are changed to 1400 Hz - 1500 Hz the frequencies which where originally in the 1400 Hz - 1500 Hz band are put in the 1100 Hz - 1200 Hz band etc. But then up to ten times a second the order in which the bands are swapped around is changed. The order in which the bands are changed is dependant upon what is known as the encryption key a number between 1 and 274,877,906,944. Even if you have a MASC radio it will not be able to un-scramble what you want to listen to unless you know this key number.

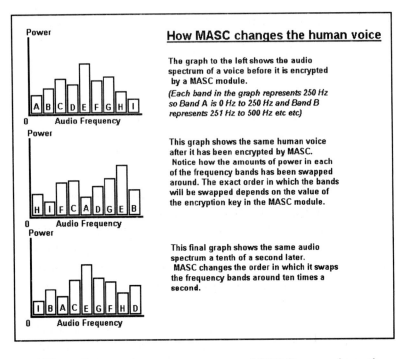

Power

A B C D E F G H I

0   Audio Frequency

How MASC changes the human voice

The graph to the left shows the audio spectrum of a voice before it is encrypted by a MASC module.

(Each band in the graph represents 250 Hz so Band A is 0 Hz to 250 Hz and Band B represents 251 Hz to 500 Hz etc etc)

Power

H I F C A D G E B

0   Audio Frequency

This graph shows the same human voice after it has been encrypted by MASC. Notice how the amounts of power in each of the frequency bands has been swapped around. The exact order in which the bands will be swapped depends on the value of the encryption key in the MASC module.

Power

I B A C E G F H D

0   Audio Frequency

This final graph shows the same audio spectrum a tenth of a second later. MASC changes the order in which it swaps the frequency bands around ten times a second.

When listened to on a scanner MASC sounds rather like listening to a drunk Donald Duck (if you can imagine that!) although some words can be picked out the majority is indecipherable. You can also recognise MASC as it transmits short data bursts each time a user presses their radios push to talk button and each time they let go. This data burst gives the radios identity number which can be decoded by a computer in the police control room which is then able to know the identity of the officer calling even before he speaks. This feature is very popular with officers as it means if they are attacked they don't have to waste vital seconds giving their callsign because they know this is already known by the control room. The data bursts have other uses as well. Because criminals can no longer listen on a scanner it is possible they could attack a police officer and steal his radio. If this does happen the control room can transmit a data burst which instructs the stolen radio to delete its encryption key and shut down. Then the radio is useless. To stop some clever criminals from transmitting a spoof data burst on a police frequency and stunning officers radios just before a robbery. Each radio will only stun itself if the base station also transmits the radios authentication code as well. The authentication code is also a number between 1 and 274,877,906,944 so the chances of a criminal guessing it are rather slim! Radios fitted with MASC can also transmit clear voice

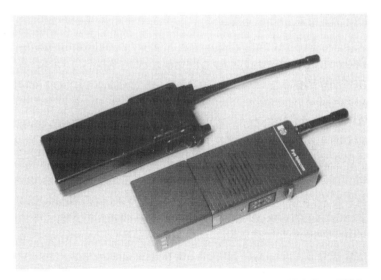

Police radios such as the Kenwood TK340 and Philips PFX can be fitted with MASC encryption modules.

so that they can communicate with radios without MASC or ones which have a different encryption key. Even when transmitting clear voice MASC still adds data bursts to the conversations. In Britain MASC is the recommended by the Home Office and ACPO (Association of Chief police Officers) and is now used by nearly all of the British police forces. Just how much MASC is used varies, most forces only equip special squads (usually the drugs squad) with MASC radios for surveillance operations. However a few forces such as Nottinghamshire have equipped every handheld UHF radio with MASC and now all policemen on the beat use it. Marconi are also busy selling MASC to other countries at the moment. I am afraid there is no simple way to descramble MASC. There are persistent rumours on the Internet from someone who has a friend who knows someone etc., who has a chip to decode MASC but these most likely are just rumours. Even if you manage to get hold of a MASC radio or module there is still the problem of the encryption key!

MASC isn't the only voice scrambling system used by the British police there are a couple of others. One of these is made by Motorola and is called DVP (Digital Voice Protection). As the name suggests this is a digital system. Each radio is fitted with an analogue to digital converter chip. The digital output of this chip is then encrypted using a mathematical formula. The mathematical encryption formula also requires an encryption key a number between 1 and 2,360,000,000,000,000,000,000. So just like MASC owning a DVP radio does not mean you will be able to descramble other peoples broadcasts you also need the key. DVP is secure enough to be used by the US Air Force and by the US Secret Service who guard the President. It is also used by the FBI and DEA (Drugs Enforcement Administration), even small town Sheriffs now use DVP. Motorola DVP is now being used for special squads by a few British police forces. The new range of DVP radios made by Motorola are known as Advanced SecureNet. Radios in this range can have their encryption key changed over the air. This overcomes a problem with the original DVP range which was that if a radio was stolen then all the other radios would have to be returned to base so they could be loaded with a new key. This could be very difficult in the middle of a major surveillance operation! However with the Advanced SecureNet radios data can be transmitted over the air instructing all radios except the one stolen to change to a new key. This can be done in seconds and the radios don't have to be returned to base. At the moment you are most likely to hear DVP (which sounds just like static) if you live near an American air base. If you are near RAF Mildenhall then try listening on 419.275 MHz where DVP has been logged. DVP radios can transmit using normal analogue narrow band FM if required. You can easily tell when a DVP radio is being used like this as a 750 Hz audio tone lasting 85 milliseconds is sent every time the push to talk button is pressed. I am afraid that there is very little hope of hobbyists being able to decode DVP encrypted radio conversations. Plenty of American hobbyists have tried using various technical methods and none have had any success. The only possible method would be if you own a DVP radio (there are now a few on the market) and manage to find out the encryption key of the system you wish to monitor. This is very unlikely!

The other voice encryption system used by British police forces is called Cougar and is made by Racal. Cougar was originally designed for use by the British Army but has sold around the world. Little is known about it other than it is digital system just like DVP. Cougar is now used by the Regional Crime Squads (who used to provide scanner owners with some very interesting listening) of all the British police forces. In a recent TV documentary the Flying Squad in Lon-

The Racal Couger Commander uses didital encryption and is used by may special Police squads.
Photo courtesy of Racal.

don could be seen using Cougar radios. As Cougar is both digital and was designed for the military I very much doubt that it will be possibly decoded by hobbyists!

The last form of voice scrambling in common use is known as time domain encryption. This works by sampling a short period of speech perhaps a tenth of a second which it then breaks into for example another ten smaller segments. It then re-arranges the order of these segments before transmitting them. The receiving radio has to correctly re-order the segments so the user can understand what is being said.

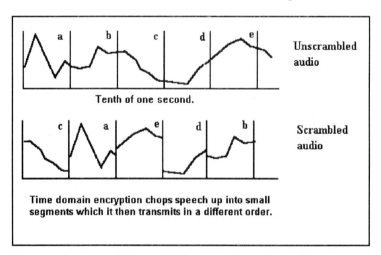

Tenth of one second.

Unscrambled audio

Scrambled audio

Time domain encryption chops speech up into small segments which it then transmits in a different order.

Encryption modules which use time domain encryption that can be fitted in handheld radios are made by a number of American companies such as Datotek and Transcrypt. In Britain there have been trials of this encryption system. In a trial period during the

Christmas of 1994-1995 British Home Stores equipped their store detectives radios with Transcrypts encryption modules. They did this because of rumours that shoplifters were using scanners to find out the location of store detectives. In the future I am sure that more security companies will be using this kind of encryption module. There have also been reports of time domain encryption modules being used in the VHF marine band by fishermen. They need them to inform other fishing boats belonging to their company where they have found fish but don't want their competitors to hear. You may also hear time domain encryption between 30 MHz and 40 MHz during periods

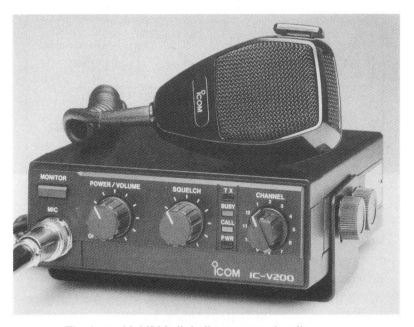

The Icom IC-V200 digitally encrypted radio
Photo courtesy of Icom (UK) Ltd.

of enhanced propagation. If you do then you are hearing the Russian Military. These encrypted conversations usually begin with someone counting in Russian before the encryption begins. The only method of I can see of decoding time domain encryption is using a fairly powerful PC fitted with a soundcard. The encrypted radio conversation could be sampled from the scanner by the PC's soundcard and saved onto disk as a sound file. It is then possible to examine the encryption system using a sound editing program such as GoldWave a popular shareware program. With a program like this it is possible to closely examine the waveform. If you look at the output of a time domain encryption system like this you will soon see points on the audio waveform where the waveform suddenly changes, this is the beginning or end of a segment. Then you can try the cut and paste facilities of the sound editor software to move the segments around. Look at this problem rather like a jigsaw examine the waveform at the end of one segment then search for another segment the start of which looks like it matches. Next cut and paste so that the segments are placed next to one another. After a while the conversation will be begin to sound intelligible. This method is however very time consuming so you should try and look for a pattern to how the segments have been moved around. If you find one and are a reasonable computer programmer then you could try and write a program which takes in a sound file and automatically rearranges the segments.

It looks certain that more radio users will soon start using voice encryption on their radio systems. Besides the police I expect many private security companies will soon be using them. But while I think digital systems are uncrackable by the hobbyist (at the moment!) I am quite certain that some analogue systems will be decoded by hobbyists before the end of the decade.

Encryption Politics   8

There is nothing to prevent modern digital radios from using almost unbreakable encryption which would make eavesdropping impossible. Indeed GSM telephones could have used encryption such as this. To find out why this didn't happen we have to go back to the second world war. Perhaps the greatest secrets of that war the Allies ability to decode the main encryption systems used by the Axis powers, the German ENIGMA encryption machine was broken by a combination of Polish, French and British cryptographers and the Japanese PURPLE system was broken by the Americans. The ability to read these messages saved tens of thousands of lives and probably shortened the war by a couple of years. It also meant that after the war signals intelligence agencies such as the NSA in America and GCHQ in Britain were given plenty of funding and had a great deal of influence in the Government. During the cold war they carried out some very ingenious and successful operations against Eastern block countries (two books well worth reading on this subject are *Spycatcher* by Peter Wright and *The Puzzle Palace* by James Bamford). However they also used their listening capability against there own population. In both Britain and the USA they read all out going telegraph messages until the 1970's. To achieve this powerful computers had to be developed to scan the thousands of telegraph messages for ones containing interesting words (such as perhaps "Vietnam") which would only then be read by humans. Although foreign governments used encryption it just wasn't a problem when dealing with civilian messages. As at the time anyone with knowledge of encryption worked for governments and were sworn to secrecy, civilians didn't have access to computers and the only strong encryption system available to them known as One Time Pads was impractical. This all changed in the mid 1970's for three reasons:-

1) The American government wanted banks to use a strong encryption system and released details of an encryption system known as the Data Encryption System (DES). For the first time civilians could look and a modern encryption system and learn from it.

2) The microcomputer revolution meant that a computer which in the early 1970's would have filled a room and would have cost millions of Pounds now could be fitted in a single chip which cost only a couple of Pounds.

3) A radical new system of cryptography known as public key encryption was discovered by American academics Whitfield Diffie and Martin Hellman. Normal encryption systems use one encryption key which is used to encrypt a message and by the person who receives the message to decrypt it. The problem is if I wanted to send an encrypted message to you I also have to send you the key. But this means anyone eavesdropping also gets the key and they can decrypt any further messages they intercept. The only

way around this is for us to meet in person so I can give you the key, but if we can meet in person then there isn't much point in sending encrypted messages is there! But a public key encryption system uses two keys the encryption key (also known as the public key) and the decryption key (known as the secret key). If I want you to send me encrypted messages I can safely send you my public key because even if it is intercepted it is no good to the eavesdropper as it can only be used for encrypting messages and can't be used for decrypting them. As long as my secret key remains secure (and I have no reason to give that to anyone !) our messages are safe. So now two people who have never seen one another before can exchange public keys and start communicating securely.

Throughout the 1980's a growing number of civilians (mainly in the USA) studied cryptography and planned possible uses for it. Then in the early 1990's a bombshell came. An American civil rights activist and computer programmer called Phillip Zimmerman wrote a program called PGP (Pretty Good Privacy). The program allows computer text messages to be encrypted by public key encryption. So if I read an interesting message posted on the Internet I can send that person my PGP public key by E mail and they can send me their key also. Then we can use PGP to send encrypted messages (which could be programs, pictures or sound samples) to each other. What is amazing is that PGP doesn't cost a penny it is free. Also Mr

Zimmerman has released the source code for PGP so other people have converted it so it runs on just about every kind of computer available ! In early 1996 a new version of PGP called PGP Phone was released which allows two people with multi media computers and modems to have telephone conversations with each other that are encrypted and are probably immune from telephone tapping.

However PGP isn't popular with everyone. The NSA doesn't like it because they say PGP could be used by drug cartels, terrorists and child molesters to escape legal telephone tapping by the police. Supporters of PGP have said however that the NSA doesn't like it because it thwarts illegal telephone tapping and threatens the jobs of thousands of people who work for the NSA. In 1993 the US government tried a new approach when they announced details of what they called the Clipper chip. Clipper chips would be cheap and could be put in computers, modems and telephones to encrypt information using an encryption system known as Skipjack which remains secret. To help keep Skipjack secret each Clipper chip is protected against reverse engineering. This is when engineers use electron microscopes and X-ray photography to discover how a chip works. To prevent this happening to Clipper chips each has a thin layer of metal above and below the chips circuit inside the chips ceramic package. This prevents electron microscopes and X-ray cameras from seeing inside. What really attracted the American government to the Clipper chip was that it uses something called key escrow. When a Clipper chip is made it is given a unique encryption key which is programmed into it. However a copy of this key is then given to the American government. This means that if a American police force try to tap a drug dealers telephone line and discover he is encrypting his conversations with a Clipper chip they go to court and ask a Judge to allow the government to release the chips key to them. If the judge allows this then they can listen to the drug dealers calls. So that large numbers of Clipper chips will be manufactured (which will lower production costs and make them cheap enough to be put in consumer goods) the US government plan to force any company who do business with them to secure their communications with the Clipper chip. As you can imagine many Americans aren't happy about the Clipper chip they believe their government should live in the real world and accept that public key encryption exists. They also argue that corrupt judges could be bribed to sign orders for Clipper keys to be handed out. But most of all they ask if Skipjack is so good why can't they examine how it works! In 1995 after growing public awareness of Clipper and a academic paper (*Protocol Failure in the Escrowed Encryption Standard* by Matt Blaze) which exposed a possible weakness of the system, the American government seem to have stopped talking about Clipper and it appears to be a low priority now. The Americans still use a law aimed to stopping the export of weapons to prevent products containing strong cryptography from being exported. For example one of the radios in the Motorola DVP range of encrypted radios uses the DES encryption system, but because DES is considered difficult to break the radio cannot be sold to customers outside the United States or Canada. Phillip Zimmerman the author of PGP was to be prosecuted under this law after PGP became widely available throughout the world and faced up to twenty years in jail but the charges were thankfully dropped.

In Europe governments are just as concerned about encryption (see the chapter about GSM phones and A5X) but the general public here seem to know less about the subject than their counterparts in America. So far only France has a law which bans encryption schemes not approved by the government but other countries seem to be planning such laws. In Britain the Labour Party have said they will introduce laws concerning encryption if they come to power.

After reading this you may be thinking that this is all very interesting but what has it got to do with what I listen to on my scanner. Well it is rumoured Motorola are planning a voice encryption system using the Clipper and that AT&T are planning to make a cordless phone which uses it. The irony of all this is that if governments pass laws forcing companies only to use weak encryption schemes in their radio communications products then all eavesdroppers will benefit. This is already happening in the field of encrypted computer communications where a group of cryptography enthusiasts (known as Cypherpunks) have been breaking messages sent using the weak encryption systems which the American government allows to be exported. Although these systems cannot be broken by home computers at the moment, the Cypherpunks are connecting lots of small computers together on the Internet. In effect this forms a super computer which can crack these weak codes in days. It will be interesting to see how long it will take before scanner hobbyists start doing this to decode intercepted encrypted messages.

Scanners in the Future 9

Soon the majority of cell phone calls will be on the digital GSM networks, a great many home cordless telephones will be DECT digital ones and by the turn of the century all emergency service radio communications will use TETRA. Some people have argued that this will mean the end of scanners. While I am sure the analogue scanner on your desk won't be able monitor many radio communications in five or ten years. I am quite certain that a new generation of digital scanners will be developed to cope with the new communications systems. This will be possible as many of the digital radio systems use publicly available standards which anyone can buy also the cost of components for a digital scanner such as DSP (Digital Signal Processing) chips continues to fall. Computer communications networks such as the Internet mean that scanner hobbyists around the world will be able to exchange information quickly, securely and cheaply. So that if a Scanner owner in Singapore discovers a useful monitoring system or gadget that information will be known by scanner owners around the world within a day. The advance from analogue radio systems to digital ones hasn't been total however. In the first edition of Scanner Busters I included a chapter on Digital Short Range Radios (DSRR). Since then however the system has been dropped for the time being, as the digital technology was just to expensive at the moment. Instead a new system called Short Range Business Radio (SRBR) has been introduced instead. These are cheap short range radios that are easy to licence and are intended for use by small businesses and such groups as hikers. To keep the price down these radios use analogue Narrow Band FM and use the following frequencies:-

49.2625 MHz Paging	49.2875 MHz Paging
461.2625 MHz Voice	461.3000 MHz Paging
461.4750 MHz Voice	461.4875 MHz Voice

So who knows perhaps the future won't be digital quite as quickly as the experts predict !

Background Reading

If you enjoyed this book you might also be interested in reading the following books:-

The ARRL Handbook, ARRL (Published Yearly)
The Puzzle Palace by James Bamford, Penguin 1983
Patrick Fitzgerald & Mark Leopold - *Stranger on the Line*, Bodley Head 1987
Jane's - Military Communications, Janes (Published Yearly)
Hitler's Spies by David Kahn, Macmillan 1978
Digital Signal Processing by Craig Marven & Gillian Ewers, Texas Instruments
European Scrambling Systems by John McCormac, Waterford University Press
Applied Cryptography by Bruce Schneier, John Wiley 1994
GCHQ by Nigel West, George Weidenfield & Nicholson Ltd 1986
Spycatcher by Peter Wright, Heinemann 1987

To find out what is happening in the world of scanning it's a good idea to read these magazines:-

Short Wave Magazine - available from news agents
Ham Radio Today - available from news agents
Monitoring Times - available from Interproducts, 8 Abbot Street, Perth, PH2 0EB.
Popular Communications - available from Popular Communications, 76 North Broadway, Hicksville, NY, 11801-2953, USA.